Shirley Kerel.

(416) 237-5240

DEEDS
OF GODS
AND HEROES

DAVID CREIGHTON
Aldershot High School
Burlington, Ontario

 EDUCATIONAL PUBLISHING COMPANY
A DIVISION OF CANADA PUBLISHING CORPORATION
TORONTO ONTARIO CANADA

ISBN 0-7715-1437-9

Previously published by Macmillan of Canada
under ISBN 0-7705-0456-6.

   10 WC 86

Printed and bound in Canada

IXORI CARISSIMAE

CONTENTS

1 What the Myths Mean   1

HUNTERS OF NORTH AMERICA

2 Wemicus the Trickster   8
3 The Buffalo's Bride   15

GOD-KINGS OF EGYPT AND BABYLON

4 Horus the Avenger   24
5 Marduk and Tiamat   32
6 Gilgamesh Who Sought Life   37

GODS OF GREECE

7 The Will of Zeus   50
8 The Olympians   58
9 Dionysus Who Gives Ecstasy   67

HEROES OF GREECE

10 Theseus and the Minotaur   78
11 Perseus and Medusa   87
12 The Labours of Hercules   95
13 Jason and the Golden Fleece   107

HEROES OF THE TROJAN WAR

14 The Wrath of Achilles   120
15 The Wanderings of Odysseus   138
16 Aeneas Who Founded Rome   159

GODS OF THE VIKINGS

17 The World of Odin   178
18 Thor and the Giants   184
19 The Death of Balder   190

Study Material   197
Pronouncing Index   217

1
WHAT
THE MYTHS
MEAN

Hunters and Farmers

Most of us want to feel part of something larger than ourselves. We get that feeling by dancing; by playing on a team; by falling in love; by watching a play; by worshipping God. All of these give us *communion* – communion with some stronger rhythm than our own heartbeat.

This desire for communion is very ancient. If you were to enter the cave of Tuc d'Audoubert in southern France, you would see the footprints of early man, preserved in the hardened clay – footprints so old that in some places stalagmites partially overlie them. In one chamber are two small statues of animals – the famous Bison Sculptures – and around them are more footprints.

Here there are only the marks of heels for, clearly, this was a dancing-floor. The dancers were hunters; and, if they were anything like the hunting tribes of today, they were dressed in the skins of animals. And the heel-dance they performed was in imitation of the bison that they hunted. This is how they achieved communion with the animals whose power they respected so much.

We will never know exactly what the ancient rituals of Tuc d'Audoubert were, although we can still observe the ceremonies of some primitive hunting tribes. And we know that usually a story is told that accompanies the ritual. We call this kind of story a *myth*.

For many thousands of years man obtained his food only by hunting for it. He had not learned how to tame the animals, or how to plant seeds in the earth, and when he did find out how to do these things his life was utterly changed. The change from hunting to farming was the biggest revolution in man's history.

The archaeologists have traced agriculture to its beginnings: the first sickle; the first flour mortar; the first carbonized grains of wheat; the first deposits of cattle bones. Consider how this new way of life must have affected man's feelings. No doubt he continued to feel communion with the animals – especially with the bull, which now pulled his plough. But now it was primarily with the soil that man sought communion.

Sky-God and Earth-Goddess

The soil is female. She gives birth to the grain as a mother gives birth to her children. She is Mother Earth, or (as in the essays of many young writers) Mother Nature. And, alongside the sickles and seeds of those earliest farms, the archaeologists have uncovered thousands of statuettes of Mother Earth.

But if the earth is Mother, the sky is Father. He sends down the fertilizing rain and the heat of the sun, and he is lord of the winds, god of the lightning-stroke.

He is also lord of men, for farming enabled men to settle down in villages that grew into towns, into cities. In the fabulously fertile river valleys of Egypt and Babylon, they learned how to construct complex irrigation systems, and to regulate these projects a strong governmental system was needed. At its head was a man of unprecedented power – the king – who was a god on earth.

So it is not surprising to see that in the oldest of all recorded myths, the dominant characters are kings, kings who are as gods. Marduk, god-king of Babylon, conquers the water-monster and establishes order; Horus, god-king of Egypt, banishes the violent Seth and rules peaceably over the land. They quell chaos – the chaos of clashing men and rampaging floods. And it is their conquest that makes it possible for the food to be grown.

With these mighty figures, more powerful than any animal, men sought communion. They celebrated the victories of the god-kings in rituals that sometimes lasted for days; and it is these ceremonies that are preserved in the myths.

Mother Earth appears in these earliest myths, as the wife of the god-king. Every spring, when the seed is committed to the earth, the Sacred Marriage between king and queen was celebrated anew, and through this ritual man experienced communion with the soil.

In some parts of the ancient world, the earth-goddess was stronger than the god-king, and sometimes the king was both her husband and her victim – to be slain like the seed which disappears when it is married to the earth, or like the grain which is scythed at harvest-time. Through the ritual of this sacrifice the people achieved an especially intense communion with the great life-and-death cycle of the crops.

The Hero

The adventures of the hero follow the pattern established by the god-kings – he conquers a chaos-monster; he has his Sacred Marriage; he rules as king. But the stories describing his adventures are not myths, for they were not accompanied by rituals; they are the exaggerated accounts of real events – or what may be called *legends*.

Legends, too, give us a sense of communion, but not with the earth or the sky. Their hero is not a god, but a man, and they celebrate not the rhythms of nature, but the man-moulding pressures of combat. For the young warrior they were an education – hearing them chanted by the epic poets, he would feel himself part of a tradition of heroism.

What the Myths Mean

Myths, and the legends that took their shape from them, are not trivial fairy-tales fabricated by simple-minded people. They have profound meaning.

The anthropologist Malinowski spent some time in the South Pacific studying men to whom myths were still very much alive. He came to the conclusion that "myth is to the savage what, to a fully believing Christian, is the Biblical story of Creation, of the Fall, of the Redemption by Christ's Sacrifice on the Cross. As our sacred story lives in our ritual, in our morality, as it governs our faith and controls our conduct, even so does his myth for the savage."

And this is what the myths are – not random curiosities, but a whole way of looking at the world. To the hunter they meant the taking on of an animal's power by wearing its skin; to the farmer they meant participation in an orderly cycle of life and death. We of the industrial nations are no longer hunters, and no longer primarily a farming people. Increasingly we are cut off from wild nature, and spreading asphalt isolates us more and more from the soil. But as long as the tilted earth whirls us through seasons of rebirth and decay, as long as man, too, lives and dies, and as long as he seeks communion with something larger than himself, the myths will have meaning.

HUNTERS OF NORTH AMERICA

Fifty miles north-east of Sudbury, Ontario, on Bear Island in beautiful Lake Timagami, live the Timagami Ojibwa Indians. It is a small band, divided into four clans each of which is named after an animal thought to be its ancestor: Beaver, Rattlesnake, Kingfisher, and Loon. Such tribes, which even into the twentieth century practise the ancient ways of the hunters, are of great interest to anthropologists, for by studying these people they are able to reconstruct the rituals of early man.

Like many other hunting tribes, the Timagami Ojibwa paid homage to the bear. Until recently they performed a Bear Dance, in which the bruin's shambling gait was imitated, and they painted bears' skulls with special designs, and then tied them to the stripped, beribboned trunks of spruce trees.

Neanderthal man, who flourished in Europe even before the period of the great cave paintings, revered the bear also. In many locations, anthropologists have found the skulls of bears arranged carefully on stone slabs – the oldest altars ever discovered. One bear seems to have had its own limbs placed beneath its snout, and, if this is so, the ritual carried out was astonishingly similar to one still practised by the Ainu of northern Japan. To a young bear, whom they have nurtured since it was a cub, the Ainu say, "Little god, we are sending you back to your father and mother. Say good things about us, and come to us again." Then they kill it, remove the head and hide, and place some of its own meat beneath its snout.

This attempted communion with the hunted animal is particularly evident in primitive art. Eskimo sculpture reveals the hunter's intimate knowledge of the hunted animals' appearance. This is seen also in Indian rock paintings, like the portrait of a moose in Quetico Provincial Park (below). The most impressive of all such representations of animals are in the Lascaux cave in France. The photograph at the right shows some of the cows, horses, bison, and deer which have been rendered so animatedly on the walls of this "Sistine Chapel" of the hunters.

Many of the paintings show arrows

Selwyn Dewdney (Royal Ontario Museum, University of Toronto)

piercing the animals' bodies. Such pictures have been explained as examples of *sympathetic magic* – by showing the arrows striking the target (or by thrusting needles into a wax doll) the hoped-for result is somehow made to happen.

This is part of ritual; and the stories that accompany rituals, as was shown earlier, are called *myths*. Some stories, not rooted in rituals, which give exaggerated accounts of actual events, are called *legends*. But others are simple *folk-tales*, fantasies told only for amusement. The Timagami Ojibwa, for instance, tell how the beaver's teeth became brown (he burnt them while releasing the sun from a trap) or how the knots of birch trees came to look like wings (Nenebec once threw a bird at a birch). Such purely imaginary explanations are not myths, but folk-tales.

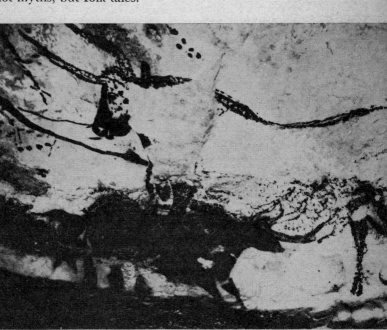

French Government Tourist Office

2
WEMICUS
THE TRICKSTER

Behind the birch-bark mask shown on the preceding page is the grinning face of a Timagami Ojibwa Indian named Benny. Once, when he was helping the author to clear a portage between two lakes in the Timagami district of Northern Ontario, Benny knocked the pulpy wood out of a section of birch, cut out eyes and a mouth, inserted a nose, and put the mask over his head for the sole purpose of scaring his friend.

In Benny we see the oldest of all figures in folklore – the trickster. Like Wemicus, he too loved a canoe race. And, though Benny could not literally turn himself into an animal, he could make a moose-call with a roll of birch bark that would beguile the ear of the wariest bull.

In Indian folklore the trickster is usually a hero. Nenebec, the Ojibwa trickster-hero, tames a troublesome wind that was making his people miserable. He provides the animals with fat. He causes a flood, by tricking the Queen of Lynxes; but he builds a raft and thereby saves the animals. Afterwards he sends out three birds, the last of which settles on the first land to appear after the waters go down. (It is now the western shore of Kokomo Bay, just east of Bear Island.)

The sadistic Son-in-law Tests of this story are probably pure folk-tale. Nevertheless, they reflect the hunters' concern with *initiation rituals*. In some Indian tribes, a boy reaching puberty is left in a remote place without food for several days so that he may receive a vision of his future. In other primitive societies, especially those of Australia, the entry into manhood is accomplished more violently.

The Burnt Moccasins

Wemicus had had many sons-in-law. This was not because he had many daughters, for he had only one. The explanation for this is that Wemicus wanted his daughter to have the best of possible husbands – an intelligent, long-suffering man, with a good sense of humour. So as soon as she found a new husband, Wemicus put him through the Son-in-law Tests. Since none of her husbands had ever been able to pass these tests, the marriages had all been brief.

Now Wemicus had a new son-in-law, smarter than any of the others. He had already passed several of Wemicus's trials with the assistance of his new wife, who by now knew all about the tests.

One morning late in the winter when the snow was still deep and sugary, she saw her husband packing gear for a hunting trip.

"Well, what does he want you to do this time?" she asked.

"He said that we ought to go out hunting beaver," the son-in-law replied.

"Oh, yes. That's what he always does at this time of the year. He didn't say which lake you were going to, I suppose?"

"No."

"He'll tell you when you get there," she said. "Now watch him carefully tonight. He might try to burn your moccasins."

"Well, that's not as bad as some of the things he has done to me."

"It's bad enough. I lost one husband that way. His feet froze, and he couldn't get home. The others all managed to get back, but they had terrible chilblains for the rest of their lives – which wasn't very long."

So the son-in-law promised to follow her advice. That day he and his father-in-law travelled a long distance to a big snow-covered lake, and camped beside it in a grove of spruce trees.

As they were finishing their supper, Wemicus said, "I don't believe I told you the name of this lake."

"Why, no," said the son-in-law, "you didn't mention it."

"It is called Burnt Moccasins Lake," said Wemicus, with a gleam in his eye. "Isn't that a strange name for a lake?" he added, laughing aloud.

The son-in-law laughed too. "Yes, imagine someone being careless enough to burn his moccasins in weather like this!"

"Say, son-in-law, that reminds me. I'm going to put my moccasins beside the fire tonight. They're soggy and should be dried out if we're going to use them tomorrow. Would you like me to put yours with them?"

"A good idea," said the son-in-law, pulling off his moccasins and handing them to Wemicus, who placed the two pairs at opposite ends of the fire. Then, since it was getting late, the two hunters lay down on their beds of spruce-boughs and covered themselves with their blankets. At once Wemicus was snoring resoundingly. As soon as the young man heard this, he got up and changed the places of the two pairs of moccasins.

The next morning the son-in-law awoke to see Wemicus busying himself around the fire. He watched with a smile as his father-in-law threw his own moccasins into the fire and then, when the reek of burning leather filled the air, he got up.

"Ah, son-in-law!" said Wemicus. "It's a good thing you got up. There's something burning around here, and we'd better find out what it is."

"It smells like burning leather," said the son-in-law.

"Maybe somebody's moccasins got burnt after all," Wemicus said, with a chuckle. "Yes, here they are – they look like yours, son-in-law! They must have fallen into the fire."

But the son-in-law was already slipping on his own moccasins. "No, Wemicus," he said. "These are mine. It must have been yours that fell into the fire!"

Wemicus took one look at his son-in-law's snugly fitting moccasins, and thrust his hands into the fire for the charred remains of the ones he had put there. With a howl of anguish he recognized them as his own.

"Too bad, Wemicus!" said the son-in-law. "Well, I'll be getting along now. Come as soon as you can!" And he picked up his blanket and started to walk home. For a while his ears were assailed by Wemicus's yells, but by the time he had trekked over a near-by hill the cries could no longer be heard.

Towards sunset the son-in-law arrived at his own wigwam, and told his wife what had happened. "It serves him right," she said. "I hope he dies. I've had enough of these tests."

But a little while later they heard the unmistakable sound of Wemicus's voice. He was singing happily, and eventually the words of his song were discernible.

"Spruce is warm," Wemicus sang, "spruce is warm."

He had wrapped his feet in spruce boughs, and was pushing a big boulder in front of him that was melting the snow – he had heated it in the fire. "Spruce is warm, spruce is warm. Ah, daughter! I want my supper!"

And, since he was her father, she was obliged to prepare it for him.

The Toboggan Slide

Spring was coming, and after a succession of warm days the snow had melted to slush. Then, unexpectedly, there came a spell of cold weather and the land was encased in ice.

"Son-in-law," said Wemicus, "we'd better go sliding. I know of a very good hill."

But Wemicus's daughter knew all about this hill, and she warned her husband. "There are poisonous snakes on that hill," she said. "But you'll be all right if you use this." And she handed him a split stick which held a special kind of tobacco. "Hold this in front of you as you go down, and the snakes won't bite you."

So the young man accompanied Wemicus to a steep, glassy incline. When they had struggled to the top of it, they stripped the bark from a dead pine tree and made toboggans. Then Wemicus pushed off, shouting "Follow me!" The son-in-law knew that they would pass close by the lair of the snakes, but he started off down the slope anyway.

He rattled down the sleek hill, and, sure enough, he saw the snakes directly in his path. They were angry, for Wemicus had roused them by sliding into their midst. But the son-in-law held out the tobacco, and the snakes, though furious at being disturbed for a second time, did not strike.

When he reached the bottom, Wemicus was waiting for him. "Good slide, eh, son-in-law?"

"Just fine," replied the young man.

"No difficulties on the way down?" said Wemicus, crestfallen.

"Not a thing."

The son-in-law had passed again.

Cracking the Lice

When summer came, Wemicus's daughter warned him about the next test he would have to endure. "Pretty soon," she said, "he'll want you to pick lice from his head. You're supposed to crack them in your teeth."

"Well, that doesn't seem too bad," said the son-in-law.

"It's bad, all right. Those aren't lice he has in his head. They're poisonous lizards."

"Well, what should I do?"

"Here," she said. "Take these cranberries. Crack them instead." So he put an emergency supply of cranberries inside his shirt.

A few days later Wemicus said to his son-in-law, "I'd like you to look for lice in my head."

"Yes, father," said the young man. Wemicus lay down, and his son-in-law began to rummage around in his hair for lice. He pretended to catch one; then he reached into his shirt for a cranberry. Pop!

"That was a big one," said Wemicus. "Get them all!"

"You have a good colony," the son-in-law said. "But I won't miss any."

So the son-in-law continued with his task – but not with the result Wemicus had hoped for.

The Gulls' Eggs

After this, Wemicus decided that it was time for the Egg-Gathering Test.

"Do you know that rocky island where the gulls nest?" he said to his son-in-law. "There are a great many eggs there. Let's collect them and have an egg supper tonight."

So they set off for the island by canoe. There was no mistaking it – a great swarm of gulls wheeled over its forested crown, and another throng lined the shore, feeding on the many dead fish that lay there. The two men nudged their canoe against the shore.

"All right, son-in-law," said Wemicus, "you go on ahead and get the eggs. You should find enough to fill our canoe."

So the son-in-law wandered along the shore in search of nests.

"You'll have to go farther inland," Wemicus shouted, "near a heap of skeletons. That's where some of my daughter's other husbands gathered eggs." Even though the son-in-law had not been advised by his wife about this test, he went farther inland anyway, and there he came across his predecessors' bones, right in the middle of the gulls' nesting-grounds.

When he looked back at Wemicus, he could see the old man gesticulating wildly and shouting at the gulls that were clustered around him. Although he was some distance away, the son-in-law heard some remarks about "that man" and "your eggs" and he heard Wemicus scream, "I give him to you. Peck him to pieces."

Then the son-in-law saw a great cloud of angry gulls flying towards him. Soon they were swirling about him, battering him with their wings and pecking at him with their beaks. But he had wisely brought a paddle with him and with one sure stroke of its blade he brought down one of the birds. This was enough to deter the others, and they flew off, squealing.

The son-in-law tore the wings from the bird he had killed, and attached them to his arms with vines. He filled his shirt with gulls' eggs, flapped his wings, and rose into the air.

As he glided across the lake he looked down and saw Wemicus moving along in the canoe, singing to himself. He was not paddling, however, for he knew how to move the canoe merely by singing. By chance Wemicus gazed up at his son-in-law, but did not recognize him, thinking that he was only an exceptionally large gull.

When the son-in-law flew into camp, his children rushed up excitedly. "Here," he said to them, untying the wings and throwing them on the ground. "You can play with these."

His wife came out of the wigwam. "What do you have in your shirt?" she asked.

"Oh, I found some gulls' eggs," he replied. "Cook them up for supper, will you?"

He sat down outside and started to smoke his pipe, and soon he saw Wemicus beach his canoe and walk up to the camp, still singing contentedly. Abruptly the singing stopped, for Wemicus saw the children playing with the gulls' wings.

"Where did you get those?" he said.

"Father let us have them," the children replied.

"Your father? But how could he? Those gulls tore him to pieces."

Then he glanced up and saw his son-in-law smoking his pipe peacefully before the wigwam. "Hello there, Wemicus!" he said. "All ready for a good egg supper?"

Wemicus was too astonished to reply, and he never did find out how his son-in-law had got home.

The Canoe-Race

Now Wemicus was down to the last of his tricks. One day he said, "This is a good time to make ourselves new canoes. Let's cut down some trees to get birch-bark."

So they went to a grove of birches and started cutting down a tree, and when they had cut it almost through, Wemicus said, "There's a game we ought to play to make the time pass more quickly. I'll sit on this side of the tree, and you sit on that side."

"Now," said Wemicus. "You say 'Fall on my father-in-law' and I'll say 'Fall on my son-in-law.' Whoever says it too slowly, or gets his tongue twisted, will have the tree fall on him."

"Fine," said the young man. So they began to yell orders at the tree. But Wemicus made a slip of the tongue, and immediately the tree crashed down on him, squashing him into the earth. Since he was a manitu – a spirit – he was not harmed, however.

So the two men cut the birch-bark, took it home, and made the canoes. As soon as they had finished, Wemicus said, "Now let's have a race." They launched their canoes and jumped in.

Wemicus had made a big sail of birch-bark, and the wind pushed his canoe into the lead at once. The son-in-law had not made a big sail, for he was afraid of upsetting his canoe, but he paddled as fast as he could, shouting encouraging words at Wemicus.

"You're going to win, Wemicus!" he cried.

"That's right!" said the father-in-law proudly. "You should have thought of this arrangement too!"

"Well, it's too late now. But you're certainly going fast!"

But the young man had turned the tables on his father-in-law this time. He knew that the sail was too big for the canoe, and that sooner or later it would capsize. And, sure enough, a strong gust of wind overturned the canoe, and Wemicus tumbled into the water.

Soon the son-in-law had paddled to the spot where the canoe had been upset. He looked down into the water, and there he saw a long, lean fish of a kind he had not seen before. It was a pike, the first of its kind, for that was what Wemicus had turned into. And that was the end of the Son-in-law Tests.

3
THE
BUFFALO'S
BRIDE

At one end of the cave of Les Trois Frères in France is a passageway a mere foot or so in diameter. It is only with the greatest difficulty that one can crawl along it – breathing is hard, the heart labours, and, as one writer has suggested, it is like crawling through a coffin. At the end of the tunnel is a great chamber engraved with hundreds of drawings of animals. Mingled with them are a few representations – rare in cave art – of men. (See the illustration below.)

These men, garbed in the skins of animals and dancing, are *shamans*. Sometimes called "medicine men", they are the ones who were believed to have special access to the spirit world, and to serve as intermediators between spirits and ordinary men. On Bear Island, for instance, one of the chief's main functions was to invoke the Great Spirit, Manitu, so that he could be sent against the tribe's enemies.

As the one who ascended into the spirit world, the shaman was often represented as a bird. The famous Dying Buffalo painting in the lower chamber at Lascaux shows the shaman with the head of a bird, and with a bird mounted on a stick beside him. The hero of the following story, too, is a shaman in bird form.

But if the shaman ascends, he also descends. In later stories, we shall see the shaman going down into the underworld to bring forth departed souls. And in this story, too, the magpie is the one that enables the dead to return.

"Wemicus the Trickster" was a simple folk-tale, told only for entertainment. But in the story of the Buffalo's Bride we enter the realm of true myth, for it reflects a serious religious ritual – the shaman, through his intense communion with the spirit of the buffalo, works upon these animals for the benefit of man.

The Buffalo Trap

The Blackfoot Indians used to kill buffalo by having them fall over a cliff. Along the two arms of an extended V which pointed to the cliff, they built rock-piles and hid behind them. The shaman then put on his buffalo-head and robe, and went out to the nearest herd.

He danced before them. The buffalo took notice of him and moved closer. The shaman, still dancing, moved backwards toward the mouth of the V. He increased his pace; so did the buffalo.

The animals came on and on, until they had gone past the first rock-piles at the ends of the V. Then the Indians who had been hiding there jumped up, shouted, and flailed their arms so that the buffalo in the rear grew excited. They galloped forward, inciting the animals in front to run also. The shaman stepped out of the way, for the herd was now stampeding past the boulder-piles, from each of which sprang screaming Indians. The buffalo thundered toward the cliff, and when they reached it there was no turning back: those in front were pushed over by the ones behind; and usually even the last plunged over in blind panic. The fall killed many of them outright. And the survivors, most of whom had broken their legs or backs, were finished off by the arrows of the Blackfoot.

So it went on for many years, and the slaughtered animals provided abundant meat and skins for the Indians. But one year the buffalo could not be driven to the fall. Again and again the hunters crouched behind the rock-piles and the shaman went out to entice the herds toward the cliff. They would follow him, and even break into a run; but they would always veer off to the side without entering the V. And now the Blackfoot were threatened with starvation.

Marriage with a Bull

Early one morning a young woman went out to get water in the valley beneath the cliff. She looked up and saw a buffalo herd feeding at the edge of the cliffs above.

"Oh, why don't you jump?" she said. "If only you will, I shall be glad to marry one of you!"

She did not mean it, of course, but to her amazement the entire herd suddenly hurled themselves over the cliff! And she was even more startled to see a great bull, who had survived the fall, gallop straight towards her. "Come!" said the bull, and he took her by the arm.

"No!" she said. "Don't touch me!"

"But you promised to marry one of us, if we jumped," said the bull. "And now, I will be your husband." And he led her up out of the valley and into the prairie.

The other Indians had heard the thunderous fall of the buffalo. Now they rushed to the spot, killed off the wounded, and cut up the animals for their first good meal in many weeks.

But soon they noticed that the girl was missing. They searched up and down the valley, but could not find her. Then her father said, "I must look for her." And he took his bow and arrows, climbed up the cliff, and went out into the prairie.

After a while he came to a buffalo wallow, where the animals came to drink and to lie in the mud. He sat down; and, as he thought about what he should do next, a magpie flew down beside him.

The man called out to the bird. "Magpie! Please help me! You can fly about; perhaps you could find my daughter somewhere on the prairie. If you do see her, say, 'Your father is at the buffalo wallow.'" And the magpie flew off to find the girl.

Now a herd of buffalo was not far away, and as the bird flew overhead he saw a young woman in their midst. Landing on the ground beside her, he said, "Your father is waiting for you at the wallow."

But the girl whispered, "Don't talk so loudly. My husband is sleeping and you mustn't wake him. Please tell my father to wait for a while." The magpie delivered the girl's message.

Just then the bull did awaken. "Go", he said to his wife, "and get some water for me."

So the girl took a horn from his head and went to the wallow; and there she saw her father. "Why did you come here?" she said. "They will kill you!"

"I must take you home," he said. "You must come with me at once."

"No!" she cried. "The buffalo would come after us, and kill us. Let us wait until my husband sleeps again; then perhaps we may escape."

Death and Revival

The girl left her father, filled the horn with water, and returned to the bull. But as soon as he drank from the horn he snorted, "Ha! There is a man near by!"

"No!" the girl screamed. "There is no one!" She was terrified.

The bull took one more swallow. Then he gave a mighty bellow. All around him, the other buffalo stood up and bellowed back. They tossed their shaggy heads, shook their tails, pawed the earth, and ran wildly about. Then they clustered together and galloped towards the wallow.

The girl, running after them, caught a glimpse of her father, white against the brown of the buffalo. Then he was down. They trampled him; they hooked him with their horns; they trampled him again. And when it was over blood stained the ground, but not a single portion of the man's body could be seen.

"Oh, my father!" the girl sobbed. "My father!"

"Ah," the bull said, "you mourn for your father. Now you know how it is with my people. Our fathers, our mothers, our children – you spare none of us. You send them over the cliff, so that they crack their spines and die in terrible pain. But I will take pity on you. Try to bring your father back to life: and if you can, you and he may return to your people."

The girl turned to the magpie. "Oh, help me!" she said. "Find just one part of my father's body, and bring it to me."

The magpie flew over the trampled mud and searched in every footprint for a particle of bone. And at last, by probing in the mud with his beak, he recovered a minute fragment, and brought it back to the girl.

Tenderly, she placed it on the ground, and covered it with her robe. Then she began to sing. It was an unearthly, mournful song; and as she breathed the words the robe began to flutter and lift. She pulled it back, and there was her father as in life. But he was not breathing.

The girl gently covered her father again, and resumed her song. And when she removed the robe again, she saw that his chest was moving. Then his limbs moved also, and he rose to his feet.

The magpie chattered happily and flew excitedly round and round. But the buffalo were struck with awe. The bull turned to the herd and said, "These are strange things. A man is trampled into nothingness and yet is brought back to life!"

Then the bull spoke to his wife. "You and your father may go. But first you are to learn our dance and song. Never forget them! For just as your father has been restored to life, so we expect you to revive our people when you have killed them."

And he led the buffalo in their dance. The step was heavy and deliberate, and as they went through the measures the buffalo sang, slowly and gravely. When they had finished, the bull spoke again. "You must not forget this ritual. Now return to your people and teach it to them. And those who do the dance of the bulls must wear a bull's head and skin. For the purpose of this ritual is to be as we are."

So, when the girl and her father had returned to the camp, they taught this ceremony to their people. And they still perform the dance and song of the buffalo, so that the herds may continue to renew themselves.

GOD-KINGS OF EGYPT AND BABYLON

The greatest of human revolutions was that which changed man from a hunter to a farmer. But although many of the hunters' old traditions were lost, others lived on. The trickster survived in figures like the Egyptian god Seth; the shaman seems to have evolved into the farmers' god-king. And in the animal-headed gods of Egypt and other lands man continued his ancient communion with majestic beasts.

The farmer's special communion was with the soil. He felt himself a part of the annual growth-and-decay cycle of the crops, and of the natural forces that fertilized them – the rain, or, in Egypt and Babylon, the great rivers. In Egypt it was the Nile that spread the rich mud upon the land. Every year the pattern was the same: in mid-summer the Nile began to rise; by mid-August the dykes were cut and the river revitalized the parched land; by mid-November the waters had fallen and sowing could begin.

Yet the Nile was not entirely reliable. If it rose too high, it might do severe damage to the dyke system; if it did not rise high enough, there would be famine. We, with our well-stocked supermarkets and grocery stores, cannot know the threat that this posed, but to these people it was an ever-present threat, and they poured out their anxieties in communion with their king, who was a god on earth.

The king's power was enormous. Merely

The Metropolitan
Museum of Art,
Dodge Fund, 1931

to hew the stone for one king's pyramid, 100,000 men laboured for ten years. So far, the tomb of only one Egyptian king, that of Tutankhamen, has been found intact; but it was so crammed with riches that it took the archaeologists five years to penetrate to the king's mummy. Getting to it was like figuring out a Chinese puzzle. Four chambers had to be excavated and then four overlapping shrines. Another four coffin-like coverings had to be removed before Tutankhamen's body – ruined by too many preservatives – was finally reached.

Every Egyptian king, while he lived, was the god Horus. As soon as he died, he became Osiris, god of the dead. The wall painting in the burial chamber shows Tutankhamen going down to the Underworld

United Arab Republic Information Services

to embrace Osiris, who is the previous king. In the right-hand section of the painting (only partially visible in the above photograph), Tutankhamen himself has become Osiris.

The death of one king and the succession of the next was dramatized in a 46-act play acted out on a barge which proceeded from place to place on the shores of the Nile. Another such Passion Play was performed annually at Abydos. It depicted Isis' mourning for Osiris, Horus's victory over Seth, and Horus's visit to his father in the Underworld.

The heroic god of Babylon was Marduk. Like Horus, he too fought a death-struggle, descended into the Underworld, and assumed the kingship.

4
HORUS
THE AVENGER

The tablet shown on p. 22 illustrates the Egyptian king Narmer's victory over the chieftain of northern Egypt. Above the shoulder of the chieftain, here being pummelled by Narmer, is a rectangle containing the statement "6,000 enemies", and at the bottom are two of these victims, floating dead in the Nile.

Above Narmer is Horus, the hawk. The two are really one, for King Narmer is the god Horus. And the enemy chieftain is actually the god Seth, for Seth is disruption. Any opposition to the order established by the king is an invitation to chaos. This event was the original overthrow of chaos, since it was through Narmer's victory, around 3000 B.C., that Egypt was unified into one country.

Seth is not disruption only, however. He is death itself, which takes away the old king (Osiris) so that he may be replaced by the new king (Horus). He is also the flail which threshes the grain (Osiris) at harvest-time, and the summer drought, which makes the rich farm land look like the desert sands – red, the colour of Seth. The rising of the Nile rescued the land from Seth's domination, but in the myth it was Seth who threw Osiris's body into the Nile, and in one of the Egyptian festivals a gold image of Osiris was filled with grain embedded in sand, sent on a voyage, then buried. Eventually the grain would sprout, and Osiris would rise from the dead.

Underlying this myth is the belief that Seth is necessary – for *death* is necessary. The seed grain has to be buried in the earth before the new shoots can arise. In the words of Jesus, "Unless a grain of wheat falls into the earth and dies, it remains alone; but if it dies, it bears much fruit." So Osiris, in whom all the forces of fertility are concentrated, must die. His body, moreover, must be hacked apart, and his fertilizing blood sprinkled upon Mother Earth. Such were the rituals that once accompanied the myth of Osiris.

Osiris

Once, men did not know how to grow their own food. They hunted wild beasts and ate their flesh; they shook fruit from trees; they stripped the edible kernels from wild grains. But the yield was meagre, and when they had exhausted the supply of food in one area they would have to move on to another.

Winter was the worst time. If the hunting was poor, and if enough fruit and grains to last until the next gathering-time had not been collected, they would starve. So they carefully hoarded their stores of food.

In Egypt as elsewhere, men had to struggle to exist, but suddenly their lot was changed. The god Osiris, son of earth and sky, descended and walked among them. They were awed by his appearance, for his face was of brightest bronze and shone like the setting sun, and his beard was black as the richest loam.

Osiris said to the Egyptians, "Take your grain, and bury it in the earth."

They were amazed. "We must save it, so that we may eat when there is no other food."

"Plant it in the soil," said Osiris.

"But it will only rot there!"

"Yes," said Osiris, "it will rot. But from the withered kernels new grains will grow in abundance."

And they obeyed him. Into the dark soil to which they committed their dead, the followers of Osiris sank their precious grain, and waited.

The miracle happened. From the sacrificed seeds sprang new plants; a film of green overspread the black loam, and soon the grains, multiplied a hundredfold, were bronze-ripe and ready for harvest. Now there was abundance, and the people of Egypt flourished. They no longer wandered from place to place in search of food; they built sturdy homes and lived beside their fertile fields throughout the span of their lives.

The soil of Egypt was rich, for every year the river Nile rose in flood, surging across the land and leaving behind a layer of black, fertile silt; but in that sun-drenched country rain seldom fell, and the flood waters had to be saved. Thus, Osiris instructed his subjects in the art of irrigation and under his command they built canals and basins to conserve the overflowing water. Men working by themselves could not have carried out such great projects; they needed unity, direction, and a sense of purpose, and these were the gifts of Osiris.

Seth

The brother of Osiris was the fierce red-haired god, Seth. He was jealous of the king, and sought to incite the people to rebellion. Since they stood firm against his efforts, he eventually had to resort to deception and trickery.

On Osiris's return from distant lands, Seth held a festive banquet in his honour. Bejewelled guests thronged the royal court. Through rooms clouded with the fumes of incense rushed servants bearing trays laden with exotic meats, wines, and delicacies, and, as the feast progressed, nimble dancing girls, thick cosmetics glistening on their eyes and lips, flung their limbs wildly to the rhythm of harp and flute.

At the height of the merry-making, the servants of Seth bore a wonderful chest into the hall. Its lavishly inlaid wood and elaborately carved ornamentation brought admiring gasps from the assembled guests.

"Who wishes to be given this splendid chest?" asked Seth. "I will present it to the man who fits it perfectly."

The company thought this an excellent jest, and when the heavy lid had been swung back they eagerly crowded about. The first man stepped merrily into the chest and lay down.

"I had better have more to eat if I am to fill this!" he cried, realizing that there were several inches of space yet to be filled. He clambered out, and another took his place.

"Would you like me to chop off the top of your head?" someone joked, as it became clear that the second man was too tall. Amid much laughter, another candidate took his place.

"He seems to have it!" one exclaimed, as the third man stretched himself out.

"No, for his shoulders fail to fit," said another. And so it went on – each candidate being either too short or too long, too wide or too narrow. And then Osiris himself decided to try his fortune.

"It fits him perfectly!" they cried in amazement. But just as Osiris, smiling happily, began to rise from the chest, a number of Seth's retainers sprang forward. They grasped the great lid and brought it crashing down over the struggling king.

In the sudden darkness Osiris could neither move nor see, and he could hear nothing but the muffled clamour outside. Breathing became difficult, although as his eyes became adjusted to the darkness he could see thin strips of light around the lid. Then came the painfully loud crack of hammer blows, as nails were driven into the wood. A hissing sound followed – molten lead was being poured along the edges of the lid. Osiris's lungs cried out for air, but he could no longer breathe. He was losing consciousness. He felt a heavy jolt, as the coffin was lifted onto the men's shoulders, and then he could feel no more.

Seth's henchmen carried off Osiris's suffocated body in its adorned case. "How easily we trapped him!" they gloated. "How perfectly his body fitted!" And indeed it did – for the chest had been deliberately constructed to his measurements.

Isis

Osiris's queen was his gentle and gracious sister, Isis. When Isis learned of Seth's treachery, she was distraught with grief, for not only had her husband been slain but she could not mourn his body. So she began a patient search for his coffin, asking everyone she met the same question.

At last her efforts were rewarded. A group of children had seen men bearing an unusual chest to the banks of the Nile where they set it adrift in the swift-flowing waters. The coffin had been borne by the river to the Mediterranean Sea and had been washed ashore at Byblos, where it had come to rest against a shrub of tamarisk. In a miraculously short time, the plant had grown into a majestic tree, the trunk of which completely enclosed and concealed the coffin. So much did the king of that country admire the tree, that he had it cut down and used as a pillar in the royal palace.

Isis travelled to Byblos and there, as she sat grieving beside a well, maid-servants of Queen Astarte came to draw water. Isis spoke sweetly to them, dressing their hair and adorning them with a strange perfume. Hearing of this, the queen asked her servants to bring the stranger to the palace. So great was her admiration for this gracious and dignified figure that she made Isis the nurse of the infant prince. Isis told no one that she was herself a queen, however, and while she awaited the opportunity to recover her husband's body she grew to love the child that had been entrusted to her care.

Isis tended the baby after a strange fashion. At night, when no one could observe, she would place the child on a bed of flames until it glowed with an ember-like radiance. Then she would assume the shape of a swallow and fly about the pillar that contained Osiris's coffin, singing a song of sad lament.

One night, however, Queen Astarte entered the room and saw her child lying in the flames. With a scream of terror she snatched him from the fire. Then Isis said in a sorrowful voice: "Why have you not trusted me? I am Isis, Queen of Egypt and wife of Osiris. I have bestowed a great honour on your household. Evening after evening I have been burning away the mortal parts of your son, so that he might live forever like the gods. But now you have broken the spell."

A look of astonishment and dismay swept across Astarte's face as she heard these words. Isis continued: "I will stay here no longer, for my work is done. But I ask you to grant me one request – that this great pillar be brought down, for in it lies an Egyptian coffin containing the body of my murdered husband."

The pillar was removed, and Isis severed the wood of the tree's stem and flung herself upon the coffin, wailing aloud.

A ship was provided for the conveyance of the coffin to Egypt. In her homeland again, Isis opened the chest as soon as she was alone, and, seeing once again the face of Osiris, she wept long and bitterly. Then she removed the coffin to a secluded spot.

But the woes of Isis were not yet at an end, for Seth, hunting wild boar by moonlight, discovered the hiding-place. Enraged, he ripped the coffin open, hacked the body into fourteen pieces, and scattered them throughout Egypt.

Isis now undertook once again the search for her husband's body. Sailing up and down the Nile in a boat of papyrus, she searched with infinite care, and found all of the pieces but one, which had been eaten by crocodiles. She then brought them to Abydos, on the Nile's western bank, where an age before the first land had risen from the waters of the Flood.

There she reunited the parts of her husband's body and, assuming once again the form of a bird, fluttered her wings over them. Magically, bone was knitted to bone, flesh to flesh; the warmth of Isis's body sealed the divisions. And then, so revitalizing was her influence that Osiris's collapsed tissues swelled, his congealed blood thawed and flowed again. Osiris had come back to life.

But no longer was he to be King of Egypt. Here at Abydos was the entry to the Underworld, and here was the Field of Reeds to which the dead would come to be judged by Osiris, for now he was the God of the Dead. Here their hearts would be weighed against the feather of an ostrich to determine whether they were lighter, and therefore sinless. And those who were without blemish would be borne aloft into the heavens, to another Field of Reeds, to that cluster of many stars that revolve slowly around Polaris, and never dip beneath the horizon, never die.

Horus

Isis now gave birth to a son, the falcon-headed god Horus. At the moment of his birth a great light burst over the world, for Horus was the sun, which soars like a hawk from horizon to horizon. But since he was at the mercy of Seth, Isis concealed him in a basket and allowed him to float down the Nile to the marshes of the Delta. There she later recovered him, and cared for him.

Horus grew rapidly to manhood, and one day the spirit of Osiris came from the realm of the dead and asked him this question: "What is the noblest of deeds?"

Horus replied immediately: "To avenge one's father or mother when wronged!" And thus did Horus vow to be avenged on the wicked Seth. To further this purpose, Osiris reappeared several times to Horus and instructed him in the ways of battle. When Horus was fully mature and agile in combat, he set forth to fight with Seth.

Red-haired Seth, determined to put down this pretender, attacked as soon as he saw Horus approach. But the falcon-god was ready for him. He flew high into the sky and hurled himself down upon his foe, slashing with his beak. Seth was stunned by Horus's strike, but he fought back, spewing violent winds at his enemy. They had little effect on Horus, and he swooped and tore at Seth, his beak tasting blood again and again.

The battle raged on for three days without a moment's rest, as the two continued to wheel and spin high above the Nile. Then Seth, scored with many wounds and exhausted, slumped to the ground. Horus bound him in chains and delivered him into the hands of Isis; then he flew off in pursuit of Seth's henchmen.

The Escape of Seth

Seth's trickery was not at an end, however, and he began to speak cunning words to Isis. "Why do you permit this youth to confine me? He does not realize that my hot winds are needed to warm this land. Surely you must know this! Will you allow Egypt to suffer famine?"

"This is deceitful," said Isis. "It is your scorching heat that turned our fertile land red and lifeless when you slew my husband!"

"You do not understand," Seth replied. "But here is something that you cannot help but see. Look at the wounds that your son gave me. See how these shackles chafe them!"

Isis looked, and saw his slashed flesh, rubbed raw by the chains. The sight roused in her feelings of compassion, but she held firm. "I pity you," she said, "but you have given my son much injury! And recall", she sobbed, "how you dishonoured the body of my husband!"

"Isis," said Seth with unusual gentleness. "Again you refuse to understand me. I did kill Osiris. But I was strong, this land needed my strength, and I had many followers who wanted me to be king! How could I go on bending my will to his? I am your brother. Surely you can sense how I felt. Now, my sister, I beg you to release me from this torment!"

And Isis, her mind a welter of emotions, removed the chains from Seth's limbs.

Seth slipped away, and soon afterwards Horus returned to find his prisoner gone. Isis murmured her explanation, but, far from satisfying Horus, it made him more furious than ever, and impulsively he swept off her head in his anger. In the same instant, however, it was replaced by the head of Hathor, the goddess of cattle – and from that time Isis had the ears and the crescent-moon horns of the cow.

The Victory of Horus

Horus then flew after Seth, and fought with him a battle that was as brief as it was fierce. Seth at once ripped one of Horus's eyes from its socket, but Horus's return attack was so savage that Seth turned and fled over the burning sands of the desert. Horus assaulted him again and again, until he had managed to snatch the eye from Seth's weakening grasp. Then he pursued him across the borders of the land.

Now Horus sought out his father. He came to Abydos, and on the Boat of the Sun sailed to the Island of the Blessed, landed on its shores, and walked through a luxuriant grove to the portals of a great mound. He entered, and descended the winding passage-way into the Underworld.

Horus approached Osiris, an austere, erect figure who clutched his sceptre and flail against his chest. He embraced his father and gently inserted into his lips the eye that had been torn from its socket.

At once, new vitality permeated Osiris's body, and from thence radiated everywhere – to the dead, and to the living in the world above. It flowed back to Horus and endowed him, the new King of Egypt, with his father's potency. And it animated the grain, newly planted in the Nile-soaked loam, causing the green tendrils of new life to burst from the withering seeds and snake upwards through the earth towards the sky.

5
MARDUK
AND TIAMAT

The ritual illustrating the myth of Marduk was the great New Year's festival of Babylon. Its purpose was to re-enact the first New Year's Day, when Marduk mastered the turbulent but vital waters of Tiamat.

Early in the festival, Marduk was said to have disappeared into the Underworld, where he fought his great battle. While he was absent, the people mourned, and ran wildly about the streets "searching" for him. Two days later he re-emerged in triumph. On the tenth day the king who represented Marduk was united with a priestess in Sacred Marriage. This ceremony, which was enacted on a pyramid-like structure called a ziggurat, was thought to ensure the fertility of the fields and animals in the coming year. In the great marriage procession the king rode in a chariot, while his consort was borne in a boat on wheels. On the eleventh day the gods were said to be setting down laws for the coming year, as Marduk had done after his triumph. And on the twelfth day the farmers began the year's ploughing, confident that all was in order.

One fascinating aspect of the festival was the "humiliation" of the king – at one point the chief priest struck the king until his tears flowed. Some have seen in this, and also in the Sed festival of Egypt, survivals of earlier rituals in which the king was slain, and his blood sprinkled like fertilizing rain upon the earth. Among the Shilluk of modern Africa, it was the custom to kill the king after he had reigned for seven years. He was slain with a maiden at his side, at the new moon, just before the rains began and the seeds were sown. And at Ur in Babylonia, evidence has been found of a royal burial in which the king was accompanied not only by his queen but by sixty-seven other women, all of whom had been buried alive. Even more gruesome mass sacrificial burials have been discovered in Egypt. Thus, it was thought, would a corrupt land be made pure.

The Birth of the Gods

In the beginning the whole world was water. There was nothing but the water – neither a reed nor a grain of sand. There was no bottom to that measureless ocean, and there was no sky, for the waters were everywhere.

The sweet and salt waters were mingled together. Apsu ruled over the fresh waters, and the salt waters belonged to Tiamat, mother of all.

For countless ages the world was changeless and motionless. Then into those waters came something that had not been – they were streaked with silt. Apsu had fathered it, and Tiamat had given it birth, and over the silt ruled the first god and the first goddess.

The strands of silt roved in the waters, thronged, congealed. Then they thickened and thickened until they split the sea, and at the limits of the world the horizons appeared: a circle of silt, and a circle of air, each with its own god. Then the dome of heaven was filled with air, ruled by Anu; and Anu fathered Ea, lord of the earth. Many other gods were to follow, but none would have the wisdom of Ea, whose eyes and ears were always open and always seeking truth. Soon there was no secret he could not surmise, no magic feat he could not perform, nor anything he did not know.

And now gods in great numbers were born. They clustered together, surging restlessly back and forth and dancing wild dances. Then Apsu and Tiamat, who had not known motion, were disturbed. Several times Apsu burst into the gods' gatherings and tried to quell their revelry, but each time he was ignored. At last he said to Tiamat, "These gods have become hateful to me."

"Yes," said Tiamat, "we have no stillness any more."

"No sleep at night," Apsu shouted, "and no rest by day! They must be destroyed!"

"You must remember", said Tiamat, "that these are our grand-children. We created them. And we must treat them gently."

"No!" Apsu declared. "I am going to destroy the gods."

But Ea knew at once of Apsu's intention. He told the gods, who cried out in dismay and rushed about all the more; then their frenzy subsided into brooding despair. But Ea had devised a plan, which he now put into execution.

Ea took a pitcher, and filled it with water. Then he chanted over it a magic spell. Still reciting the magic words, he made his way to Apsu.

Ea took Apsu unawares, and poured the magic waters over him. It was like drenching him with sleep, for immediately Apsu became drowsy; then he began to slump forward, and in a few moments he was in a heavy slumber. And at once Ea pounced on him and put him to death.

Not for long did Tiamat remain unaware of Ea's deed. When she discovered it, she flew into a towering rage, and immediately gathered together the forces of vengeance. Eleven monstrous beings she created, whose mouths were filled with fangs like snakes, and about whose bodies flickered sheets of flame. No blood ran in the veins of these creatures, for they were filled with venom. At their head she placed her new husband, Kingu.

The gods entreated Ea to act as he had done against Apsu. Again he strode forth. But when he saw the horrible light sheathing the monsters' bodies, he fled in terror.

Ea's father Anu was now called upon to defend the gods. Anu advanced directly toward Tiamat; but when he saw her ferocious glare, he too retreated.

"Who can save us now?" said the gods. "Great Anu cannot face these enemies, and even Ea in all his wisdom could not stop them!"

But there was one who was greater than either of those gods.

Marduk

When Ea had vanquished Apsu, he had established a dwelling-place in his victim's body and there, in the very heart of Apsu, a son was born to Ea's wife. He was born fully grown, and taller than any of the other gods. In appearance he was magnificent – fire shot from his lips, and lightning from his eyes. This was Marduk, greater than any god before him.

Immediately the gods chose him as their new defender. He was brought before their assembly, and he spoke these words: "If I am to conquer Tiamat and save your lives, you must proclaim me chief among the gods. From this time forward all decisions shall be mine, and whatever I decree shall not be altered!"

Marduk's demands were satisfied; the gods made for him a throne, where he sat in triumph. "You, Marduk, are chief among us!" they chanted. "From this time forward all decisions shall be yours, and whatever you decree shall not be altered!"

They placed a garment before Marduk. "Reveal your powers, Marduk!" they urged. "Speak, and the cloth shall vanish. Speak but again, and it shall return."

One word from Marduk's flashing lips, and the garment vanished. Another, and it was restored.

"Marduk is King! Marduk is King!" the gods exclaimed joyously. And on Marduk's head they placed a kingly crown.

Marduk now armed himself for combat. At his side he hung a marvellous bow and a quiver of gleaming arrows. For protection against Tiamat's enchantments, he rubbed red powders on his face and hid a sacred herb in his tunic. To ensnare Tiamat, he made a giant net, and then he mounted the chariot of the winds, and set the lightning before it. With the mace of the thunder in his grip and a fearful radiance flashing from his face, Marduk rode forth against Tiamat.

Tiamat

Kingu and his army of monsters, seeing Marduk sweeping towards them, gave in to utter panic, and fled. But Tiamat stood firm.

"So you are the choice of your elders!" cried Tiamat. "They have placed their trust in you and given you all power! Meet me in single combat and die!"

Then Tiamat seemed to lose her senses. Shrieking curses and spells, her legs shaking terribly, she lunged at Marduk, her jaws open to consume him. But he was ready for her. Into her gaping mouth he drove the storm winds, and the swirling blasts forced their way down her throat, and tore into her belly. Tiamat felt her body swelling and tried to close her jaws, but it was too late, and the winds kept them wide apart.

Marduk gathered his net and flung it over the helpless Tiamat, so that she was completely enmeshed in its coils. Then he drew his bow, and sent an arrow into that cavernous mouth; it ripped through the sinews of her body and pierced the heart. Tiamat's colossal body flinched, and slumped dead at Marduk's feet.

Marduk took in his hands the mace of the thunder and brought it down on Tiamat's skull, sending blood spurting forth. The North Wind carried her life blood to far places. Then Marduk split Tiamat's huge body into two parts – from one he made the earth and the other he raised up to form the sky.

In the sky Marduk placed lights. He made the moon a creature of night, and each month gave her a crown; but the sun he made superior, and at its approach the moon's radiance would dim. Finally, Marduk placed the stars in their constellations, and to every part of the universe he sent a god, to be its ruler.

Man

When Kingu and his gruesome followers had seen Marduk's approach, they had fled, trembling with fear. But before they could escape, Marduk had hurled a net over the struggling mob. And when Tiamat had been vanquished, he destroyed their weapons and bound them in chains.

Now the gods gathered around their leader, and said, "To all of us you have assigned a post and a duty. But who will provide us with food and tend our dwellings? We must have servants to sustain us while we perform our tasks."

"This I will do," announced Marduk. "I will make bones and arteries, and construct a puppet to toil for us. I will call this puppet Man."

"There is no need to make new bones and flesh," counselled Ea. "Let Kingu provide them."

So Kingu was brought forth, and put to death. His body was slit open, and from his blood and bone Man, the servant of the gods, was formed.

One last labour the gods undertook. They constructed for Marduk a city, Babylon, and in its midst a temple. Here Marduk set forth the laws and destinies of the universe. Here Marduk and the goddess of the seed-time were united in Sacred Marriage. And here, at each New Year, Marduk's kingship was reaffirmed.

6
GILGAMESH
WHO SOUGHT
LIFE

The story of Gilgamesh illustrates an ancient theme, one that goes back into the Hunting Age, of man as the master of animals. Enkidu is another survival from the days when the hunt was all-important. He is shaggy, like the skin-clad Blackfoot hunters. But he also seems to be the sacrificial victim of the Mother Goddess, and, as might be expected, he rebels against her, just as Gilgamesh does.

Here we see the origins of a new kind of hero – one who breaks away from the woman-dominated rituals of the early farming societies. The price he must pay for this is a high one, for he loses the gift of immortality thereby – the plant of life is confiscated by the snake. Both of these are often associated in the myths with the Mother Goddess; they go together to form a sinister combination. Frequent mention is also made in these myths of an underground passage, as here in the case of Siduri.

Despite its references to ritual, this story may well be a *legend* – that is, a tale based partially on actual events. The cedars guarded by Humbaba have been linked to forests in Syria whose wood was coveted by the inhabitants of treeless Babylonia. And the king-list of Erech, a city which was indeed ringed by magnificent walls, includes the name "Gilgamesh".

The Gilgamesh story is also the first of the *epics,* which are long poems recounting the adventures of a hero. This deeply moving story, the ancestor of great epics like Homer's *Iliad* and Virgil's *Aeneid,* is of immense importance in the history of literature.

Enkidu

Gilgamesh, unrivalled in might, was king of Erech. Only one-third of him was human, and the rest was god. No one could oppose him in combat.

Because of his unchallenged power, Gilgamesh enslaved his people. Old men performed the hard tasks of the fields, unaided by their sons, who were required to labour on the great walls that surrounded the city. Finally, when the arrogance of Gilgamesh became unendurable, his oppressed subjects prayed to the gods for deliverance.

In answer to their prayers, the gods created a being as strong as Gilgamesh. His name was Enkidu. Raised with a herd of wild animals, Enkidu wandered from place to place jostling with them at watering-holes. As his hair grew to shaggy lengths, he began to look more and more like a wild beast himself.

The people of Erech, who had not been told of Enkidu, soon discovered that the animals that stumbled into their traps were being released. One day a hunter came upon Enkidu as he was performing an act of mercy. He went to Gilgamesh, and told him of the great wild man who behaved like an animal.

The king soon hit upon a plan to put a stop to Enkidu's activities. And, several days later, as Enkidu neared the hunter's territory, he saw a strange creature, the sight of which filled him with a new and powerful emotion. He wanted to embrace it and it seemed to welcome him as he approached. He bounded forward and took it in his arms, and, for the first time in his life, he had embraced a girl.

But when Enkidu ran from the girl to rejoin the herd a change had come over the animals; they backed away from him and raced off across the plains. Gilgamesh's plan had succeeded.

Enkidu, bewildered, returned to the girl. "Why do you live with beasts?" she said. "Come with me to Erech, a city of men." And so the girl led him to Erech.

As Enkidu and the girl entered the city, they heard the clash of cymbals, the whistle of flutes, the cries of a great throng of people. It was the beginning of the New Year, and the festival was nearing its climax – the Sacred Marriage of king and goddess. A great burst of cheers from the crowd – and Gilgamesh himself approached.

Suddenly, Enkidu was struck with a strange excitement. With a whoop, he leaped into Gilgamesh's path and stood there menacingly. The crowd stared unbelievingly at the wild stranger, but Gilgamesh, having been warned in a dream of this rival, at once braced himself for combat.

With incredible swiftness, Gilgamesh ran towards his enemy. But the charge did not weaken Enkidu and he attacked, galloping like a bull. Gilgamesh nimbly stepped aside, and Enkidu crashed into a door-post, shattering it.

Now Gilgamesh grappled with his shaggy opponent. They butted each other like wild rams until, finally, Enkidu gained a secure grip. He bent Gilgamesh's body into a taut, quivering arc. Suddenly Gilgamesh's knee buckled; Enkidu had won.

Enkidu did not gloat over his victory, however. "You are raised up above men," he said to Gilgamesh. "Kingship is yours. Never again shall I oppose you." They embraced, and an indestructible friendship was formed.

Humbaba

Enkidu became a hunter, and joined his new comrade in the search for game. Far afield they roamed, over grassy plains and rugged mountains. One day Gilgamesh said to Enkidu, "In the cedar forest of the mountains lives fierce Humbaba. Let us kill him, and rid the land of his evil presence."

But Enkidu replied, "I have heard of Humbaba. His roar is the storm wind, and wherever he breathes, there is death! Whoever goes to the cedar forest is seized with a mortal weakness!"

"Who does not succumb to death?" said Gilgamesh. "Only the gods have life everlasting. Man? He is a puff of wind. Already you fear death. Where is your heroism? I shall go ahead, and, if I fall, I shall have this fame: 'Gilgamesh fell against mighty Humbaba!' This shall be my immortality, though I, and my sons, shall die."

Enkidu was persuaded. They armed, and set out for the cedar forest, taking but three days for a journey that would ordinarily have lasted six weeks. When they arrived, they gazed in silence at the lofty cedars that reached upward in green magnificence towards the mountain peaks, and then they entered the forest.

Gilgamesh seized his axe and brought a cedar crashing to the ground. Humbaba heard the noise, and ran in anger from his lair. "Who is this?" he bellowed, in a voice like the rushing winds of a tempest. "Who is felling my trees?"

As the heroes had hoped, Humbaba came crashing through the forest towards them. They saw his face, his hideous skin falling in rope-like folds, his eyes glassy and staring. And they saw the monster roll his head about, trying to fix Gilgamesh in his deadly gaze.

Gilgamesh called out to the sun-god for aid and immediately, Humbaba was blasted by a hot whirlpool of winds. In that swirling tempest he could neither advance nor retreat, as white-hot winds scorched his eyes.

"Help me!" he wailed through rattling teeth. "Release me and I shall be your servant!"

But Gilgamesh and Enkidu, taking no chances, closed in on the writhing monster and, with their swords, hacked off its gruesome head.

Ishtar's Revenge

Gilgamesh now washed the grime from his hair and replaced his soiled clothing with a handsome cloak. When he had set a kingly crown on his brow, he appeared so irresistible that even Ishtar, the goddess of love, came to his side and spoke to him temptingly.

"Gilgamesh," she whispered. "Be my lover. My house is fragrant, and when you enter, the very threshold will kiss your feet." Drawing closer, she attempted to win him with inviting glances. "You shall be above all the princes of the world. A chariot, a chariot of gold and silver, shall be yours!"

But Gilgamesh sat in stony silence, displaying no emotion. Then he said, "What has become of your lovers? In your youth, there was Tammuz: every year there is wailing for his fate. The herdsman – how he doted on you! But you transformed him into a wolf, so that his own dogs attacked him. The gardener who resisted your charms – you bound him in a net, where he cannot move. That is doubtless what you intend for me. You are a pool that turns muddy, a shoe that pinches, a palace that crumbles on those who enter!"

Ishtar, now roused to fury, flew up to heaven to her father Anu. "Father!" she screamed. "Gilgamesh has offered me insults! He has dared to mention my past lovers! Send down the Bull of Heaven upon him! Immediately, or I will break open the doors of the Underworld, and send the dead – more numerous than the living – back into the world!"

"You know", Anu replied, "that the appearance of the Bull means a famine of seven years?"

"There will be food enough," she answered fiercely.

So the Bull of Heaven was sent hurtling down upon the two heroes. But Enkidu leapt to his feet, and, even as the animal snorted foam in his face and lashed him with its tail, he grasped its horns and held them firmly. Gilgamesh drew his sword and thrust it into the Bull's neck. The Bull of Heaven had met a swift death.

Ishtar, who had been watching the encounter, let forth a shrill curse. "Woe unto Gilgamesh!" she shrieked. Then Enkidu compounded the insult to the goddess by ripping off the Bull's right thigh, and casting it in her face. By this insolence, Enkidu had sealed his own doom.

After the triumphal return to Erech, and the celebrations in the royal palace, Enkidu lay down to sleep. He had a terrifying dream. The gods were in council, and they were seeking to determine who should die for the slaying of the Bull of Heaven. At one moment, Enkidu was condemned; at another, Gilgamesh. On through the night the gods quarrelled, and, though Enkidu awoke before a decision was reached, he became certain of his own imminent death when he was unable to rise from his bed.

For nine days he lay there, growing weaker and weaker. Gilgamesh strove to encourage him, recalling the days of hunting when they had scaled mountains together in quest of leopard and panther. He spoke of their victory over the monster Humbaba, and praised Enkidu for the destruction of the Bull of Heaven. But he felt increasing anxiety as he saw Enkidu's staring eyes, his greying flesh.

And then the day came when Gilgamesh reached out to touch Enkidu's heart, and no heartbeat could be felt.

"What a fearful sleep is this!" Gilgamesh shouted. "You cannot hear me!" He threw off his rich clothing, tore at his hair, and roared his grief. Through the night he could see the appearance of his friend changing – his flesh shrivelling, his wild beauty passing.

"This, then, is death," he lamented. "And I shall be like Enkidu when I die!"

Siduri

After seven days of mourning, Gilgamesh left the palace and embarked on a journey across the plains to the very end of the world, where lived an old man named Utnapishtim. This was the only mortal who had gained eternal life, and Gilgamesh was determined to learn his secret.

The journey was long and gruelling. His garments were ripped away by the rough bushes and he had to grapple with lions and use their skins for clothing. Eventually, however, he reached the Mountain of the Sun.

In the depths of the Mountain of the Sun was a long and gloomy tunnel, through which Gilgamesh would have to pass. Its guardians, men with the tails of scorpions, challenged him. "Do not think to traverse this tunnel," they said. "Only the sun, in the course of the night, makes this passage: no mortal has ever done so."

"Open your gates!" Gilgamesh roared. "I fear no danger here." And the gates opened for him.

As soon as he entered, the gloom engulfed him. Soon he could see nothing ahead of him, and nothing behind. But Gilgamesh strode boldly onward, though the darkness made his journey seem like a dream. At first, he felt as if he were hardly moving, and then it seemed as if he were descending into the mouth of death, that he would forever be walking towards his doom. He cried out in terror, as his mind yielded increasingly to this fear.

Suddenly a breeze touched his face. Then he saw a pinpoint of light! Gilgamesh ran joyously to the outlet and emerged from the mountain into a wondrous garden – a marvellous garden indeed, beside a blue-green sea. Through eyes dazzled by the splendour about him, Gilgamesh beheld trees and vines spangled with precious gems. Here leaves were of lapis lazuli and thorns of glowing pearl. And here lived a woman named Siduri, who squeezed the juice of grapes into golden vats. She saw Gilgamesh, and was startled by his appearance. "Why is your face so sunken, and your flesh so worn? You have suffered great woe, I can see."

"He who with me underwent all perils," replied Gilgamesh, "he whom I loved as a brother – Enkidu – has met the fate of men. Seven nights I wept for him, hoping like a fool that he might yet rise at my pleas. I would not let his body be buried. Then I saw a maggot fall from his body. Now I too fear death! And I seek Utnapishtim, who has overcome it."

"Gilgamesh, why do you wander?" said Siduri. "Immortality, which you crave, you will never find, for when the gods created man death was his portion: life they held for their own. Gilgamesh – fill your belly, dance, make merry day and night. Wear fresh garments and bathe in soft waters; look upon your children and embrace your wife. This, and this alone, is the lot of man."

"What comfort can I have? How can I be at rest? My friend has turned to clay! Am I, like him, to lie down and never rise again? Siduri, tell me how I might reach Utnapishtim!"

"He lives", said Siduri, "across the sea. But these are the Waters of Death, and no man but yonder boatman has ever crossed them. Go to him – he is your only hope."

Utnapishtim

The boatman instructed Gilgamesh to cut 120 long poles for the crossing: for once a pole has been lowered into the Waters of Death, it must not be used again. Having obtained the poles, he boarded the vessel and set forth.

With each thrust that Gilgamesh made, the craft was sent sweeping across the waters. One by one the poles were left behind, as the Mountain of the Sun receded further and further into the distance. Despite the speed at which the boat was being propelled, however, Utnapishtim's island could still not be seen, and the poles were rapidly diminishing in number.

Finally, when the last one had been used, Gilgamesh removed the shirt from his back and held it up, using his arm as a mast. Finally, his efforts were rewarded and the island came into view.

As soon as Gilgamesh stumbled ashore, he sought out Utnapishtim to make his request. "You have conquered death. How can I, too, obtain eternal life?"

But Utnapishtim tried to turn the hero aside from his quest by asking: "Do you expect a house to last for all time? Does a river stay in flood forever? Does the butterfly, when it leaves the cocoon, live more than a day? Nothing is permanent! Even one sleeping – has he not the appearance of death?"

"You, Utnapishtim," persisted the hero, "you are like a man; but you have been given life everlasting! Tell me your secret – how you have become like the gods."

"Gilgamesh," he said hesitantly, "I will reveal to you my secret, though it is known only to the gods and to myself. Once, long ago, the gods determined to destroy man in a great flood. Had it not been for the warning of Ea, I too would have perished. But through the walls of my reed-hut Ea whispered, 'Build a ship, Utnapishtim; and take upon it all living creatures that are yours.'

"I did as I had been told, and early one morning, when an awesome cloud appeared, I entered the ship and sealed it up. The weather grew terrifying. There fell a blackness, lit only by torches of lightning, so that no man could see his neighbour. The wind struck, shattering the land like a cup. And then the waters fell, filling the land and, in the end, drowning the mountains. Even the gods were horrified, and flew up into the heaven of Anu, there to cringe like dogs.

"For seven days the flood-winds swept the land, and then there was an end. All living things had died, except what I had saved. When I opened a hatch, and light poured down, I bowed low, and wept.

"A mountain-top appeared above the waters and my ship drifted onto it. After seven days, I released a dove. But there was no resting-place, and it returned. I sent forth a swallow, and it, too, came back. Finally, I let loose a raven, and it did not return.

"I led forth my family and animals to the mountain-top, and offered a sacrifice of thanksgiving. The gods smelled the sweet odour and swarmed like flies about me. Ishtar herself appeared, lifted up her great jewels, and said, 'You gods! By this lapis lazuli about my neck, I will not forget these days; always will I be mindful of them.'

"I was led back onto the ship, and there the gods bade me kneel, with my wife at my side. And then these words were spoken over our heads: 'Before this, Utnapishtim has been mortal. From this time, Utnapishtim and his wife shall be like the gods. Far away shall they dwell, at the mouth of the rivers.' "

The Fatal Sleep

Gilgamesh sat glumly, considering with bitterness the story of the flood. Now he knew that Utnapishtim had no secret wisdom to impart, that only special circumstances had given him immortality. His quest had ended in failure.

But Utnapishtim took pity on the dejected hero. "Gilgamesh," he said, "try to defeat death by the power of your will. Refrain from sleep for seven nights."

So Gilgamesh sat on his haunches and began a silent fight against sleep, which is death in disguise. He struggled under the burden of his eyelids, fought to keep his mind from crumbling into blankness, tried to shake off the numbness gripping his body. But sleep, like a woolly mist, enfolded the exhausted wanderer.

"Look at this hero!" laughed Utnapishtim. "He seeks life, yet not for one night can he stave off sleep. When he awakes, he will deny that he has slept. Wife, bake a loaf of bread every day that he sleeps, and place each beside him."

After seven days of profound sleep, Gilgamesh awoke. As Utnapishtim had predicted, he tried to pretend that he had dozed off for a few moments only. But Utnapishtim showed him the loaves.

"Look, Gilgamesh, at the tale of your slumber. This loaf beside

you is fresh: it was baked yesterday. But the second, from the previous day, is mouldy. The third has turned white; the fourth is
soggy; and the fifth is like leather. The sixth, which is completely
dried out, was baked seven days ago – when you began your
slumber!"

"What shall I do?" cried Gilgamesh. "The Reaper has claimed
me. Wherever I sleep, wherever I step, lurks death!"

The Plant of Life

Gilgamesh washed himself, donned fresh clothing, and returned
to the boat. Just as he was about to depart, his host's wife said,
"Utnapishtim, he has come here at great labour and pain. Will you
now give him nothing for his toil?"

"Gilgamesh," said Utnapishtim, "there is a plant like a rose on the
bottom of the sea. If you can find it, that plant will restore your
youth."

In a fury of excitement, Gilgamesh tied heavy stones on his feet
and lowered himself into the sea's depths. He found the plant!
Grasping it firmly, not caring that its barbs cut his hands, he released the stones from his feet and returned to the surface.

"This", he shouted exultantly, "is a possession beyond words!
Whoever eats of it, no matter how old he is, will become young. I
myself will taste it. But before that, I will take it to Erech, to let the
old men find their lost youth!"

Gilgamesh returned across the Waters of Death, and began the
difficult march to Erech. At the end of the first day he halted at a
spring. Leaving the precious plant on the bank, he bathed in the
cool waters.

As Gilgamesh swam, a snake smelled the plant, came up to it,
and carried it off. As soon as the snake had eaten it, his skin fell off,
for it had regained its youth.

When he discovered what had transpired, Gilgamesh sat down
and wept. "For whose sake", he moaned, "have I laboured? For
whom have I spent my heart's blood? No blessing for me – I did
the snake, who grovels in the earth, good service, and now the fate
of all men shall be mine."

GODS OF GREECE

The great temple of Athena, the Parthenon, is girdled by a yard-high band of sculpture, one-tenth of a mile long. The subject of the frieze is a ritual procession in honour of the goddess; the climax of this procession, depicted on the eastern end of the temple, is a tableau of the twelve gods of Olympus. Athena, Hephaestus, Poseidon, Apollo, Artemis, and Aphrodite are all depicted in the section of the frieze shown on the following pages.

There must have been a great variety of such rituals in Greece, for the country was not a unit, as were Egypt and Babylonia with their flat, even terrain. It was split up by ribs of mountains and arms of the sea into many independent states, each having its own rituals. Few descriptions of these ceremonies have come down to us, however. In Egypt and Babylon, accounts of the great state festivals have survived, but little information is available on the Greek rituals, beyond that provided by Pausanias's travel guide. And it was written around A.D. 170 – at least two thousand years after the rituals began to take shape.

It is therefore hazardous to reconstruct the rituals behind the myths, although some clues to their significance have been discovered. Since many images of the Mother Goddess have been found in the earliest farming settlements, she must have been dominant at one time. In Crete, the emblems of the Mother Goddess – plant of life, snake, labyrinth – are especially evident. And, judging by the early Greek myths, the sacrifice of kings was also widespread among primitive farming people.

Then the land was invaded by a new race

Greek National Tourist Office

of warlike herdsmen. These people, the Mycenaeans, were the first actual "Greeks"; they were later followed by the Dorians. Their god was thundering Zeus, and they made him supreme over all others in the land. But Zeus, unlike the Hebrews' god Yahweh, did not simply eliminate the old Earth Goddesses – he married them. And in this respect he is like the god-kings of Egypt and Babylon.

Here, perhaps, is the reason why the Greek myths are more varied and more interesting than those of any other people. They arose from a dynamic conflict between two peoples, one dominated by goddesses and the other by gods. The period of conflict extended from 2000 to 1000 B.C. although until recently little was known about what was happening in religion during these years. Documents from the period

Royal Ontario Museum, University of Toronto

had survived, but in a language no one could decipher. Then, in 1954, this "Mount Everest of Greek archaeology" was scaled by a young Englishman using code-breaking techniques developed during the Second World War. His translations revealed that during the time of the Mycenaeans, Zeus and Hera were already "married", and that the cults of Athena, Artemis, Poseidon, Hermes, Demeter, and Dionysus had begun to flourish. It was thus probably the later, more domineering, Dorians who brought with them the other Olympians: Ares the god of war, Apollo the archer, and Hephaestus the forger of weapons – warriors' gods all. There is one god who survives from the time of the ancient hunters, however, for Hermes, the wing-footed messenger who escorts the souls of the dead, is clearly a shaman.

7
THE
WILL
OF ZEUS

The Greeks formed one branch of a powerful race that invaded countries all the way from India to Europe, and are therefore called the Indo-Europeans. Their chief deity was a sky-god, a flasher of lightning. In Greece he was called Zeus-pater (Zeus-father), in Italy, Ju-piter, and in India, Dyaus-pitar.

The career of Zeus is similar to that of Horus and Marduk. He has a troubled youth, he overcomes a chaos-monster ("Typhon" is another name for Seth), he has several Sacred Marriages, and he rules over Olympus. Cronus, too, seems to have been patterned on an Asian model. He wounds his father in the same way that Kumarbi, the Hittite god, had done. He brings forth children from his own body, again like Kumarbi, who produces a stone giant who grows until his head bumps against heaven. And this giant stands on the shoulders of another giant who is very much like Atlas.

So perhaps the stories of Typhon and the Titans are largely borrowed from Egypt and Babylon. But the Titans could also, as some scholars maintain, be the gods of an older generation, overwhelmed by the invading Greeks. The Indo-European tribes entered Greece from the north, and it is in northern Greece that the battle with the Titans is set. This is where Mount Olympus raises its peak above the rain-clouds to provide a base for the forces of Zeus. The Titan Prometheus is certainly a figure from a much older generation, for he is the ancient trickster-hero of the hunters. And like so many of these god-like individuals, he provides man, by theft, with the supreme gift – fire.

Uranus

In the beginning was Chaos, unending nothingness. And out of Chaos arose Gaia, the earth, who presently gave birth to the sky, Uranus, to cover her on all sides. Uranus showered rain upon Gaia and the rain-waters gathered into streams, the streams into rivers, the rivers into lakes, and the lakes into seas. Grass and trees flourished and animals roamed the earth.

The first children of Gaia and Uranus were the Hundred-handed Giants, with fifty heads and a hundred arms. Next to appear were the huge Cyclopes, each with one enormous wheel-like eye in the middle of its forehead under a great arch of eyebrow. And then came a superior race, the Titans – the twelve majestic and beautiful forces of nature.

But Uranus hated his children. He feared the grappling power of the Hundred-handed Giants and the rebellious spirit of the Cyclopes, and he envied the grace and beauty of the Titans. He therefore banished all of them to the innermost regions of the earth. From time to time one would emerge, only to be forced rudely back by the stern and wary sky-god.

Angered by her husband's cruelty, Gaia secretly appealed to the Titans to rebel against their father, and she offered them an enormous sickle made of hardest flint as a weapon. Cronus, the youngest and craftiest of the Titans, volunteered.

Cronus

Cronus first took an oath of his brothers to accept him as leader if he should deliver them. Then, at night, when Uranus descended upon the earth, Cronus waited in ambush and slashed at him with his sickle. Bleeding from his wound, Uranus recoiled in pain and ascended to his own lofty regions, never again to approach the earth.

Cronus now released the Titans from their subterranean prison. The Hundred-handed Giants and the Cyclopes, however, he was content to leave underground.

Although Cronus was king of the Titans, he was tortured by a deadly fear – the fear of being dethroned, as his father Uranus had been, by one of his own children. Against his better judgement, however, Cronus married his sister Rhea, and soon, to his dismay, their first child was about to be born.

What should be done with it? His father had banished his offspring to the innermost regions of the earth – but Cronus had another method. He would swallow his child as soon as it was born.

One day Cronus saw Rhea holding the new-born child. He did not waste any time. Snatching it from her embrace, he opened wide his mouth and thrust the squalling infant down his throat. Rhea screamed at him in anguish and the baby continued to cry inside his stomach, but for a time Cronus had quelled his fears – no child of his was going to overthrow him.

Another baby came along, however, and another, and another, and another. And each time, over Rhea's shrill protests, Cronus thrust it into his mouth. Rhea grew more and more desperate, and, finally, when yet another baby – the sixth – was about to be born, she devised a plan to outwit her husband.

She fled to the island of Crete and here, beside an unruffled lake, within a cave high on the slopes of a mountain, she gave birth to a son. She named him Zeus.

Zeus

Knowing that Cronus would be searching for her latest child, Rhea prepared to return to him. But she left Zeus behind in the care of Gaia, his cradle hanging high up in a tree. To prevent Cronus from hearing the baby's cries, she had armed warriors dance around the cradle, shouting, singing, and clashing their spears against their shields.

"Well, where is our latest child?" demanded Cronus, when his wife had returned.

Tenderly, Rhea placed in Cronus's hands a rounded object wrapped in soft clothes. He promptly gobbled it down.

"Heavy brat," he grumbled. Indeed it was, for he had just swallowed a huge stone, carefully wrapped in baby's garments.

Zeus, when he came of age, was urged by Rhea to seek vengeance on his father. She made him Cronus's cup-bearer, and provided him with mustard and salt to be added to his father's nectar. One day, when Cronus had been drinking, Zeus handed him the special mixture, and he bolted it down. So violent was its effect that all five of Zeus's brothers and sisters – along with the stone – were vomited forth.

Cronus was so ill that all of the children managed to escape, but they knew that their father, with the aid of his Titan brothers and sisters, would soon seek them out and attempt to destroy them. They therefore took the initiative, and declared war on Cronus and the other Titans.

For ten years the battle raged, neither side able to gain the advantage. The forces of Zeus were outnumbered, since they faced, in addition to the twelve original Titans, the many sons and daughters since born to them. What they lacked in numbers they made up for in perseverance, however. Finally Zeus made a momentous decision – to release from captivity those monstrous sons of Uranus, the Hundred-handed Giants and the Cyclopes.

This decision proved to be the turning-point of the war and the battle now rose to its climax. The Hundred-handed Giants made magnificent allies, for they could hurl three hundred stones in a volley. And the Cyclopes, overcome with gratitude at their release, fashioned effective weapons for their friends. To Zeus they presented the most devastating weapon of all – the thunderbolt.

The earth shook under the impact of warriors' feet and the volleys of stones flung by the Hundred-handed Giants. Everywhere whirled the thunderbolts of Zeus, scorching the earth, setting vast forests ablaze, and sending hot blasts of air spinning over the battlefield. Against all this fire-power the Titans were helpless, and they fled in disorder into the distant west. Only Atlas, their commander, was caught, and in punishment he was forced to bear on his back the weight of the sky.

Typhon

Zeus's trials were by no means over, however, for Gaia was infuriated by the humbling of the Titans, who were her most handsome children. She therefore gave birth to an instrument of revenge, the monster Typhon, who was by far the largest of her children. His arms were three hundred feet in length, for legs he had two wrestling serpents, and from his shoulders rose a hundred snakes, each with flaming eyes and a different voice: a lion's roar, a bull's bellow, a ram's bleat – an entire zodiac, and more.

Like a hurricane Typhon swirled across the Aegean to Mount Olympus, where Zeus had established his throne. He saw the monster coming and at once threw a barrage of thunderbolts at him, but Typhon caught them in mid-flight, and hurled them back at his assailant, all the while spewing forth fiery rocks from his hundred mouths.

Zeus seized the sickle of Cronus and leapt from Olympus, slicing at Typhon in his fury. Shouting, circling about each other in mid-air, the two were impelled by combat to a mountain in Syria, and here Typhon gained the advantage. He caught Zeus in the grip of his writhing serpent-legs, wrenched the sickle from him, and cut off the sinews of his hands and feet. Then, after hiding the sinews in a cave and appointing a dragon to guard them, Typhon returned to Greece.

Zeus would have remained immobile for ever, had not goat-footed Pan come along, and with a terrible roar sent the dragon fleeing in panic. The sinews were refitted to Zeus's limbs, allowing him to return to the fray.

In the interval, however, Typhon had come under the influence of the Three Fates. These are the goddesses who manipulate the thread of our lives: one spins it, another measures it, and the third cuts it off. They had offered Typhon a fruit which, they said, would restore his diminished strength. Actually, it spelled his doom. He still had tremendous power, and when Zeus appeared he hurled whole mountains at him, but Zeus threw out a veritable fence of lightning-bolts and deflected them painfully back upon the monster. Finally, Typhon retreated westward across the Mediterranean, and Zeus picked up the entire island of Sicily and brought it down upon his back. Below the ground, where the land bulges up into Mount Etna, Typhon lives still, occasionally spitting forth a stream of flaming stones.

Prometheus

Early in the war one of the Titans, foreseeing that Zeus would win, had gone over to his side. It was he, in fact, who had advised Zeus to release the monsters. This Titan's name was Prometheus, which means "forethought". His brother, whom he had also persuaded to join Zeus's forces, was called Epimetheus, and his name means "afterthought".

Until this time there had been no mortal creatures, but now the gods fashioned them, from a mixture of earth and fire. Prometheus and Epimetheus were ordered to allot to them suitable attributes, which the gods provided.

"Let me equip them," said Epimetheus to his brother, "and you can inspect my work." To this arrangement Prometheus gave his consent.

Epimetheus began with the animals. He gave speed to some, nimbleness to others, and strength to a favoured few. Some he encased in armour, while others were given a thick hide and a warm coat of fur. Those that were not equipped with hooves or claws were given tough foot-pads on which to walk. Epimetheus worked busily, distributing the different attributes, and eventually his supply was exhausted. Nothing had been left for the last of the creatures, who was man.

Man had no special strength or swiftness, nor did he have a warm covering for his body or the benefits of hoof and claw. When Prometheus came to inspect this last-created being, he was deeply distressed, for he saw that this was a noble creature, who walked with spine upright and whose brain had the potential to be creative – but he was so weak and fragile!

"One thing I would like to give him – one thing," Prometheus thought. "With it he might warm his meagre skin. It would make food soft for his teeth, it would harden his bricks and his pottery, mould his metals, and give him light. But no – he would never be allowed the use of fire. Zeus would never permit it." Prometheus knew full well that anyone who shared the fire of the gods would be punished wretchedly.

Prometheus could also foresee how Zeus would respond to a direct plea on man's behalf. "Men?" Zeus would laugh. "Those puny beings? Blot them out, Prometheus, and try again!" The very thought of Zeus's contempt for lesser creatures troubled Prometheus and he brooded for days over the future of man before making his resolve. He would steal a spark of the divine fire.

First, Prometheus plucked the stalk of a giant fennel plant – its pithy hollow could harbour a burning coal and yet conceal it as well. Then, at night, he made his way to Mount Olympus. Great ragged clouds brushed past its peaks, ghostly except when they swirled close to the gods' hearth-fire on the summit, and its glare turned them the colour of honey. Laboriously he climbed Olympus's jagged flank, higher and higher, until he was able to see his way by the glow from the palace of the gods. He crept farther upwards, to the very top of the mountain, and on through the portals of the gods' dwelling-place.

One of the gods was beside the hearth. This was Hestia, whose constant duty was to keep the fire from dying out; so serious was her responsibility that never could she marry. While she sat with her back turned towards him, Prometheus scooped a glowing ember from the fire with his fennel-stalk, and then sped from the palace, down the slopes of Olympus, down to the humble world of men.

Prometheus knew that his theft would not long go undetected. He worked feverishly to instruct his creature in the proper use of fire, and had the pleasure of seeing man's life, indeed his very soul, enkindled by the divine element. At night, the tiny flickers of his fires punctured the darkness. Zeus saw them and at once summoned Prometheus to answer for his actions.

"Did you steal fire from the hearth of the gods?" said Zeus, in a voice shaking with rage.

"Yes, it was I," Prometheus replied.

"Why did you take it?" Zeus roared.

"Because I knew that without it man would be helpless, and that you would fail to heed his sufferings."

Zeus turned to his followers. "Take this malefactor," he thundered, "and nail him to the rocks!"

"You choose to be tyrannous," said Prometheus, "like your father Cronus, and his father Uranus before him. Your fate will not be unlike theirs. None of the gods knows what that will be, for I alone have this knowledge."

Then Prometheus was carried off for his punishment to a desolate place in the Caucasus mountains, and there he was fixed to a crag by a stake driven through his body.

For many months Prometheus endured the pain of his impalement, the fire of the sun, and the piercing needles of the night's cold. And then, one day, Hermes, the messenger-god, appeared.

"Father Zeus sends me," Hermes said. "He bids you reveal his fate."

"I know his fate," said Prometheus, in a voice rusted by the elements. "I know that Zeus will some day father a son who will overthrow him. And I know what marriage-match would yield such a son. But I will reveal none of these things."

"This is the same obstinacy", said Hermes, "that brought you to your present bondage."

"Yes," said the Titan, "and I would prefer this to the slavery of being a messenger of Zeus."

"No doubt it is better to be enslaved to a rock!"

"It is thus that I return insolence with insolence."

"You are mad!"

"And you are a child, to linger here expecting anything of me!"

"My words have not softened you," said Hermes. "And now your pain shall begin in earnest. First Father Zeus will split this crag with thunder and lightning and dash you to its depths. After a weary time fastened within this chasm, you will be brought forth. And then an eagle will come every day to gnaw away your liver, for in the night it will grow whole, so that it can be torn again. Consider this, and never value stubborn pride above true wisdom!"

"I knew all this before you said it. Let him begin, let him drop the lightning-bolt upon my head, stagger the earth to its root, and hurl my body down to Tartarus, for never can he give me death!"

And no sooner had his words ended than the earth began to shake.

8
THE
OLYMPIANS

When the worshippers of Zeus swept into Greece, they began to subdue the religion that they found there – the cult of the Earth-Mother. It took a long time. Zeus "married" many of the ancient Mother Goddesses, and took Hera, the most powerful, as his official wife. Once all-important, she became secondary – and she did not like it! Surely Hera's conspiracy against Zeus refers to a rebellion by the worshippers of Hera against the Zeus-worshippers.

There was some compromise. Of the twelve deities who ruled on Olympus, six were male and six were female. But the goddesses were clearly subordinate. Athena, for instance, seems to have descended from a Cretan goddess associated with snakes or a sacred tree. But in her new role she was represented as being a mere offshoot of the dominant god: she was born from the head of Zeus. Aphrodite, too, who corresponds in many ways to the powerful Ishtar of Babylon, was born from male blood.

Two of the ancient goddesses retained their power. Artemis, who often appears on Cretan works of art, is the formidable Diana with whom St. Paul had to contend. And Demeter, whose very name means Earth-Mother, was honoured annually in the most elaborate festival in Greece, the Thesmophoria. Its rituals were climaxed by the reaping of an ear of wheat in a blaze of light. At Eleusis, where the festival was staged, the caves which represented the Underworld may still be seen. Persephone's sojourn in that dark realm probably paralleled the period of four months during which the seed-grain was stored in huge underground bins. At seed-time it was brought forth again, like Persephone.

Demeter is still worshipped today as St. Demetra – a figure whose sainthood is not recognized by the Church. In 1802 a huge statue of the goddess was removed from Eleusis and carried off to Cambridge University, where it still remains. This distressed the peasants of Eleusis to such an extent that they rioted for days – a striking example of man's yearning for communion with the soil.

Demeter and Persephone

At the end of the war against the Titans, Zeus and his two brothers drew lots from a helmet to decide the division of the universe. Zeus became Lord of the Sky, and ruled on Mount Olympus, whose snow-hung rocks cut into the sweeping cloud-fleets. Hades became King of Tartarus, the Underworld, where the souls of men would swarm after death. And Poseidon won the sea.

Poseidon spent little time on Mount Olympus, for he had his own palace of gleaming gold, deep in the waters of the sea. There he ruled his kingdom with a three-pronged staff of office, the trident, and there, in his vast underwater stables, he kept beautiful white horses, with hooves of bronze and manes of gold.

The three sisters of Zeus – Hestia, Demeter, and Hera – all became Olympian goddesses. Hestia, of course, tended the god's hearth-fire. Demeter, goddess of all that springs from the soil, provided man with vegetables, fruit, berries, and grain. It was she who showed him how to extract the kernels of grain from the chaff, to mash them, and to mix them with water.

Persephone, Demeter's beautiful daughter, loved the flowers which her mother had designed. One day, while gathering some, she discovered a narcissus of extraordinary size and beauty – a hundred blossoms growing from a single stalk. Amazed, Persephone reached out and plucked it, and instantly the black earth opened at her feet, the chasm widened, and against the black came the gold of a chariot and the deeper black of mighty horses. In the chariot was a god.

Hades, the god of the Underworld, grasped the terrified girl by the wrist and flung her into the chariot beside him. She screamed, the horses plunged into the crevice, god and maiden disappeared, and the earth closed up. Everything had happened in a moment.

Demeter heard Persephone's cry and came hurrying to look for her, but the flower-fields were empty and strangely silent. Panic and the pain of loss gripped her. Casting aside her head-dress and her robes, she took the form of a bird, searching over land and sea for a trace of her daughter.

As her futile search continued, the vegetation of the earth suffered through neglect. The leaves turned yellow, withered, and fell. Men collected the fruit that had fallen to the ground and ate it before it rotted. Finally, none was left, and it was not long before the meagre supplies of grain that had been stored ahead were also exhausted. The animals, finding food hard to get, grew leaner and leaner, and the weaker ones began to die. The existence of man himself was threatened.

Zeus became alarmed at the blight that had stricken the land. Hades had asked him for permission to marry Persephone, and Zeus, unwilling to offend his brother, had not refused his request, but now he sent a messenger to bid Hades release Persephone.

Down went Zeus's messenger into Tartarus, the depths of which are so difficult to comprehend that, if an anvil falling from the sky were to take nine days and nights to reach the earth, it would take yet another nine days and nights before it reached Tartarus.

When Zeus's message had been delivered, Hades smiled sadly. "Return then to your mother, Persephone," he said. "But as I am a brother to Zeus I am not a bad husband. Return to my kingdom and great honour will be yours." Then, harnessing the horses to his golden chariot, he handed the reins to the messenger, who returned Persephone safely to her mother.

Overcome with joy, Persephone leapt into her mother's arms. But, even as they embraced, Demeter asked her daughter if she had eaten any food in the Underworld, for anyone eating there would have to return to that grim land. Yes, she had eaten – four seeds of a pomegranate!

For so slight a sampling of the food of Tartarus, must Persephone live there forever? The decision was up to Zeus. This he decreed – that for each seed she had eaten she must spend one month in Tartarus as Hades' queen. For the other eight months, however, she could live with her mother.

Now that Persephone had returned to her again, Demeter's soul was at rest, and she set to work to revive the life of the earth. Vegetation reappeared in a mist of green, soon to condense into a ripe rain of fruit, vegetables, and grain. Mankind was saved, but now he would have to store his crops to tide him over the time of death when Persephone was in Tartarus.

Hera

Hera, the third of Cronus's daughters, became the wife of Zeus – and what a tempestuous marriage that was! Ironically enough, Hera was not only the wife of the chief god, but also the goddess of marriage, even though her greatest problem was keeping a sharp eye on her own husband. To keep track of Zeus, Hera resorted to spying and scheming, and whenever Zeus discovered Hera's activities he would flare up into a violent rage, frequently even directing his thunderbolts at her.

Like his father, Cronus, and his grandfather, Uranus, Zeus felt insecure in his rule over the gods and goddesses of Olympus, and to compensate for this bragged incessantly about his own power. One day he announced: "I am the mightiest of the gods. If you wish to test my power, fasten a golden rope to me and pull on it, all of you, and try to drag me down. You can't do it. But if I felt so inclined, I could pull you up without a moment's hesitation and hang you from a peak of Olympus."

Finally, Hera decided to do something about Zeus's arrogance, and that night, when he had fallen asleep, she called the others to his bedside, and they quickly bound him with a hundred knots. He awoke, and in his fury proclaimed that he would wreak his vengeance on all of them, but they only laughed at him, for his thunderbolts had been placed beyond his grasp. One of the goddesses came to his aid, however, and sought the help of the very individual who could best untie a hundred knots – a Hundred-handed Giant!

Quickly released by his many-armed rescuer, Zeus took his revenge. Sharp-tongued Hera was strung from the sky with golden bracelets about her wrists and an anvil hanging from each ankle. There she wept and screamed in her anguish, but no one could help her. Eventually Zeus released her, but not before exacting an oath from all the Olympians never to challenge his authority again.

Hephaestus

Two sons were born to Hera, one of whom was Hephaestus, the god of the forge. When his mother saw him for the first time, he seemed so deformed and sickly that she pitched him off Mount Olympus. Fortunately, he fell into the sea, where two sea-goddesses caught him. They reared him in an underwater cave, where he set up a forge and earned his keep by turning out hundreds of delightful metal ornaments.

One day, when Hera saw a sea-goddess wearing one of Hephaestus's trinkets, she inquired, "Who could have made you such a charming brooch?"

"Why," the sea-goddess replied, "one day a crippled little fellow was thrown our way, and we have been looking after him ever since. He is terribly clever with his hands!"

Hera's attitude toward her son changed abruptly, and she demanded that the goddesses return him to Olympus at once. There she set up an excellent forge for Hephaestus, with twenty bellows going full blast day and night. Better still, Hephaestus was provided with the most beautiful of all goddesses for his wife, Aphrodite.

Aphrodite

When Uranus was wounded by the sickle of Cronus, drops of his blood fell into the sea south of Greece. White foam gathered where they fell, the foam grew into a gleaming cloud, and suddenly a goddess sprang from within. Aphrodite, the goddess of love, had come into being.

She rode the waves in a great sea-shell, and was wafted by a gentle west wind to the island of Cyprus. There, when she stepped ashore, fresh grass sprouted miraculously from the earth, and beautiful maidens clothed her, for her beauty was too dazzling for human eyes. Then to Olympus Aphrodite came to become the wife of shaggy, deformed Hephaestus.

Ares

Aphrodite was not entirely pleased with her ugly new husband, however, and she soon found someone much more to her liking – Hephaestus's brother Ares, the god of war. Ares was most unpopular with the other gods. Not only did he have a disgusting taste for bloodshed, but he had also shown himself to be a coward, and would bellow in terror if bettered in war. Nevertheless, Aphrodite befriended him and, as a result, Hephaestus became suspicious and decided to set a trap for them.

He forged a bronze net, remarkable not only for its strength but also for its fineness of texture, for it was as thin as a spider's web. He then hung it from the roof-beams and took his leave, saying to Aphrodite, "Good-bye, wife. I am going away for a few days' vacation."

Watchful Ares wasted no time in entering Hephaestus's house, and the goddess of love rushed into his arms. Down fell the net!

So cunningly had it been contrived, that the two could not move a limb – they were caught in mid-embrace.

Hephaestus had not been far off, and now he limped into the doorway. His roars of anger brought all the gods running (though the goddesses were too modest to look in). How they laughed at the bewildered lovers and the raging husband! One of them asked, "How would you like to be in Ares' predicament?"

"Let the nets be three times as many," was the reply, "and let everybody be looking on, the goddesses too, and it would be a pleasure."

Eventually Hephaestus, still shouting in indignation, released his captives. But as soon as they were free, they scampered out of sight, too fast for lame Hephaestus.

Athena

Zeus, like Aphrodite, was not always faithful to his marriage vows, and one of his escapades brought him considerable trouble. Just as one of his mistresses was about to have a baby, he was warned that this child would be wiser than its father. To prevent the child from outwitting him or usurping his authority, Zeus decided that there was only one thing to do – swallow the mother.

But as soon as Zeus had performed this deed, he developed a severe headache. His head, it seemed, was about to split. The pain finally became so intense that Zeus asked the god of the forge to perform immediate surgery with his axe. Thereupon, Hephaestus split open his head and, with a great shout, out sprang Athena in full armour.

Now that the child had finally been born, she indeed proved to be wise – though Zeus's fears of being overthrown were unfounded. In fact, Athena became the goddess of wisdom.

From the beginning, she was equipped with the weapons of war and she was therefore well fitted for her task of defending the greatest of Greek cities, Athens. On the rocky heights of the city a home for Athena was built in later times – the most beautiful of temples. Since she never married, it was named the "maiden's apartment" – the Parthenon.

Since Poseidon also wanted control of Athens, it was decided that the city should be awarded to whoever could provide it with the more useful gift. Poseidon struck the ground with his trident and out leapt a horse. But Athena, with a touch of her spear,

caused a small green shoot to spring from the ground and immediately assume the shape of an olive tree. There was no doubt in
the judges' minds – this was indeed the greater gift. Athens was
hers.

Artemis

When Zeus fell in love with a Titaness called Leto, his wife was
infuriated. Hearing that Leto was to bear Zeus a child, Hera
determined to make life as miserable as possible for her, so she
caused a serpent, Python, to pursue Leto all over the world.

Leto rushed from country to country, but nowhere was she
allowed sanctuary, for everyone dreaded Hera's wrath. Finally,
however, she found refuge on the tiny Greek island of Delos. The
island, until this time, had floated, but now Zeus anchored it to
the bottom of the sea by means of four great pillars. Here Leto
gave birth to twins, Artemis and Apollo.

Artemis, like Hestia and Athena, never married. Hunting was
her all-consuming interest; for this reason she is called the goddess
of the hunt, although she is also known as the moon-goddess.
Armed with bow and arrows, the strong but beautiful goddess
would range the mountains, accompanied by her band of nymphs
dressed in bear-skins.

Artemis was known as the maiden-goddess, and though she had
many suitors she vowed to remain unwed. On one occasion, however, while bathing in a stream, Artemis suddenly realized that
she was being watched. A young hunter, Actaeon, had happened
to be standing near by when she had arrived, and had been foolhardy enough to remain in the vicinity. In an instant, Artemis
transformed him into a stag and his own pack of hounds tore him
apart.

Apollo

Apollo, the twin brother of Artemis, became one of the greatest
of the Olympians. As soon as he was born, he demanded a bow
and arrows, and then he sought out Python on a mountain called
Parnassus. A few arrows from Apollo's bow, and the monster was
mortally wounded. Twitching violently, it dragged itself to Delphi
and there on the mountain-side it died, pierced by Apollo's shafts.

Beneath the two enormous cliffs of granite, high up the flanks of Mount Parnassus, Apollo built his temple. From lands near and far men came, seeking advice about their future, which the famous Oracle of Delphi could provide.

The priestess of Apollo sat on a tripod – a three-legged stool – above an opening in the temple floor where volcanic vapours hissed forth from a cleft in the earth below. When the Oracle inhaled the fumes and chewed on the leaves of the laurel, she went into a trance. Her eyes glittered, her hair stood on end, and her whole body shuddered. Then she uttered wild, unintelligible sounds which the temple priests interpreted.

Apollo was the god of the sun and his chariot was drawn by fiery horses in a continuous journey across the sky, into the ocean, under the earth, and back into the sky. He was also the god of light and the source of illumination to artists, poets, and musicians. At the Pythian Games, held at Delphi in commemoration of Apollo's victory over Python, prizes were awarded to the victors, not only in such sports as boxing and horse-racing, but also in the art of poetry.

Hermes

Hermes was the son of Zeus by another Titaness. He was born at dawn in a mountain cave near the city of Corinth. By noon, tired of his cradle, he jumped out and walked to the entrance of the cave, where he spied a turtle. Delighted with the strange creature, Hermes took it into the cave, slew it, and made of its shell the frame for the world's first lyre. He improvised a song describing his mother's love affair with Zeus, and one praising himself for having been born, and when he became bored with the lyre he set out in search of adventure.

In an open meadow near Mount Olympus Hermes found a herd of cattle. His appetite whetted, he decided to drive off fifty of them. To confuse anyone investigating their disappearance he made the cattle walk backwards, and plaited twigs on his own feet to disguise his tracks.

When Hermes had driven the cattle to Pylos in southern Greece, he kindled a fire. Then, snapping the spines of two cows, he sliced their bodies into twelve equal portions, which he roasted over the fire as sacrifices to the twelve gods of Olympus: Zeus, Poseidon, Hestia, Demeter, Hera, Hephaestus, Aphrodite, Ares, Athena, Artemis, Apollo, and himself.

Hermes returned just before dawn to his cave and, after his six-hundred-mile adventure, decided that he was ready for a sleep in his cradle. His mother, suspecting that he had done some mischief, scolded him, but to no avail.

Apollo, the indignant owner of the cattle, was not long in appearing at the cave, where he beheld Hermes sleeping innocently in his cradle. "Why did you take my cattle?" he roared.

Feigning innocence, Hermes took up his lyre and played and sang such music that Apollo laughed for very pleasure.

"You clever imp," he said, "where did you learn to play like that?" In reply, Hermes graciously offered him the lyre.

So delighted was Apollo with his new possession that he gave Hermes a position he was to love – that of Messenger to the Gods. Equipped with wings on his sandals and on his cap, and with a winged staff bearing entwined serpents (the Caduceus), Hermes was kept busy running errands and guiding travellers. He was called Old Heapy because of the piles of stones he placed along the roads to serve as landmarks. But the job that consumed most of his energy was that of guiding the souls of the departed to Tartarus.

Apollo made Hermes swear never to steal the bow and lyre he had given him. But, while he did keep this oath, he was unable on later occasions to refrain from "borrowing" Apollo's arrows, Ares' sword, Poseidon's trident, Zeus's sceptre, and Aphrodite's girdle.

9
DIONYSUS
WHO GIVES
ECSTASY

The horse-tailed satyrs shown here cavorting with Dionysus are of ancient ancestry. Their origin may be traced to those early hunters, dressed in the skins of animals, whose dances are pictured in the caves of France. And they survive to this day. In certain parts of Greece their successors (now called *callicantzari*) every year dress themselves in goat-skins and leap, dance, and drink their way through their community.

It is during the twelve days of the Saturnalia that these revels are carried on. This period corresponds to our Twelve Days of Christmas – during which similar antics may be observed in our own communities. They illustrate man's timeless urge to escape from himself into something bigger and wilder.

Men could achieve communion with Dionysus by drinking wine, which represents his blood, but he is also at the root of another, more profound type of communion – that of the theatre. The Greek drama grew from the *dithyramb*, a leaping, three-step dance accompanied by a frenzied hymn, sung by a *chorus*, which told of Dionysus' life, death, and resurrection. At the Dionysiac festival of 534 B.C., a man called Thespis added an "actor" – someone who carried on a dialogue with the others. Then Aeschylus added a second actor, and drama as we know it was born.

Tragedy means "goat-song", and the chorus that performed the dithyramb usually wore goat-skins. They performed on threshing-floors, for Dionysus was also the god of the harvest, and this is where the flails hacked him apart at harvest-time. Thus tragedies end in death. But they are strangely exhilarating, for in them fear for one's own existence and pity for the suffering god come together and are thereby cleared away. This annual purification of mortality-flawed man is called *catharsis*.

Dionysus' death-struggle was not the only incident in his ritual, for he too had his Sacred Marriage. Herein lies the origin of the other form of drama, *comedy*, which usually ends in marriage rather than in death.

Semele

Zeus had fallen in love once again, this time with a girl named Semele, and Hera, even more furious than usual, decided to play a fatal trick on her rival. Disguised as an old woman, she appeared to the girl and asked Semele the identity of her husband.

Taurgo Slides

"Why, my husband is none other than Zeus, the king of the gods," Semele replied.

"Zeus?" Hera exclaimed. "You have been duped, my child. The man you married is an impostor. Ask him to reveal himself in all his glory, ask him to show you his thunderbolts, and his true identity will be revealed."

Semele was troubled. Perhaps her husband was an impostor after all! The next time she saw Zeus, she demanded that he reveal himself in his true splendour, that he show her his thunderbolts. Zeus refused. What Semele did not realize was that she, a mortal, would be consumed by their dazzling fire.

But Semele was insistent, and when she saw that Zeus could not be swayed she accused him of being a mere pretender. This was too much for the great pride of Zeus. With a blazing thunderbolt, Zeus revealed his true nature – and Semele was burned to death in an instant.

Astonishingly however, her unborn son survived that terrible flame, and Zeus, at the cost of some discomfort, sheltered the baby until it was ready to be born. He made a hole in his side, and there he placed his son. Three months later the boy, Dionysus, was born again.

Hera was not finished yet. One day while Dionysus was at play, two Titans, their faces chalk-white, burst in and snatched him up, tearing his tiny body to shreds and throwing them into a cauldron of boiling water. In such a manner did Hera attempt her revenge.

But this was not the end of Dionysus. Rhea, who had so cleverly saved the lives of her babies from the cruel Cronus, endeavoured to save even this unfortunate child. She tenderly pieced together the torn fragments of his infant body and miraculously reinfused them with life.

Midas

The young Dionysus was taken to the mountains of northern Greece, where he might grow to manhood, and here he made a great discovery, a discovery of such import that it made him a god.

Heavy clusters of grapes grew on the mountain slopes, and Dionysus loved to eat them. He would gather great handfuls of them and squeeze their juice into his mouth. Where they were most abundant, he would crush quantities of grapes into containers. After the purple fluid had been allowed to stand for several months, its flavour became even more exhilarating. He had discovered wine. Dionysus had become a god – the god of wine.

Dionysus had some rowdy friends in the mountains, who greatly appreciated his invention. Snub-nosed creatures they were, these "satyrs", with the tails, hooves, and pointed ears of horses. After bolting down great draughts of Dionysus' wine, they would invariably get into mischief.

One of the satyrs, Silenus, was older, fatter, and drunker than any of the others. Although he usually rode a donkey because he was too tipsy to walk, he had a certain amount of wisdom and was for a while Dionysus' teacher.

One night, however, Silenus, hopelessly inebriated, stumbled into the rose garden of King Midas. When servants found him next morning in the damaged flower-beds, they considered it a cause for great hilarity, and, after adorning the old toper with rose garlands, they carried him to their king. Midas treated Silenus to a round of gaiety for ten days, and then escorted him back to Dionysus' dwelling-place.

"Ah, welcome back, Silenus," cried the god of wine. "So you have been in the care of King Midas. What request can I grant this good monarch for his hospitality?"

Midas was delighted, for it seemed that the great god was ready to fulfil any request! "Let everything that I touch", he said rashly, "be turned to gold!"

"Very well," murmured Dionysus, knowing full well what would happen. "You may see that your wish has been granted."

Midas grasped at an oak branch and instantly it was transformed into shimmering, tinkling gold. He picked up a stone – and it was a nugget. He patted his dog in his delight and, to his astonishment, it became a perfect statue. Amazing – but also somewhat disturbing.

King Midas decided to celebrate by feasting. He touched his knife and it turned to gold. He picked up a piece of bread and was shocked at what happened. He reached out for a glass of wine, and tried to swallow some before it was transmuted, but he could not do it, for as soon as the wine touched his lips it turned to liquid gold. Stricken with terror, he spat it out.

Now the king knew that he would starve to death if the curse of the golden touch could not be removed. Fortunately Dionysus was merciful. "Go to yonder river," he said. "Cleanse your head and body in its waters, and you will wash away this unlucky power."

Midas did so, and he lost the golden touch, but the river sands turned a bright gold, as they are still today.

Orpheus and Eurydice

The female followers of Dionysus were called "maenads" – "wild women" – and wild creatures they were. Completely possessed by the spirit of wine, singing with head turned back, and dancing in a frenzy to the sound of flute and drum, they followed the god in riotous processions over the mountains.

In their hands they carried smoking pine torches or staffs tipped with pine cones and wreathed with ivy. By striking the earth with these staffs they could cause wine to spring forth in a fountain; by hurling them like spears, they could frighten away men. Some carried snakes in their hands or on their hair, and some, beside themselves with wine, would tear apart the bodies of animals and eat the pieces of raw flesh. The story of Orpheus shows just how violent they could become.

Orpheus, son of Apollo, was the greatest of musicians. With his lyre and his matchless voice, he created music capable of soothing and overpowering any creature. Hearing those divine sounds, men sank into a trance, seeing nothing, numbed to everything but the beauty of Orpheus's music. The wild animals within range of his voice would be drawn irresistibly towards it to mingle with their former hunters at Orpheus's feet. Even the trees, it was said, would reach out with their branches towards these enchanting sounds.

One that Orpheus overpowered with his music was Eurydice, who became his wife. Great was their happiness, while it lasted. While she was still but a bride, however, a snake bit her ankle, and she died in agony.

So great was Orpheus's grief that he determined to follow Eurydice to the Underworld, and to implore Hades himself to yield her up. The only way he could enter that dread realm, except through death, was to descend into the cave of Mount Taenarum, in southernmost Greece, and such a descent Orpheus made.

When he had completed this incredible journey, and reached those unfathomable depths, there were still obstacles to be overcome. Surrounding the land of Tartarus was the River Styx, that fearful stream over which only the dead could pass on the raft of foul-tempered Charon.

For Orpheus there was no means of entry to Tartarus – except one. He placed his thumb on the strings of his lyre, and struck sounds that even Charon could not resist. He fell under a spell, and without even knowing what he was about he ferried the living man across the waters of Styx.

The second obstacle was as easily overcome. The dog Cerberus, any of whose three heads would have devoured him in an instant, slumped forward in a swoon, soothed by Orpheus's music.

And so Orpheus entered the Underworld. The bloodless dead about him were transformed by the divine sounds, and as he played even the tortures of the damned ceased for a time. Sisyphus – condemned eternally to roll a massive boulder up a rocky slope, only to have it push him back just when he was reaching the top, and so be forced to let it rumble to the bottom again – was released from his monstrous labour. The wheel of fire on which Ixion forever whirled was for a few precious moments cooled and halted. The Danaides, who had murdered their husbands, entranced by his music, were given rest from their task of filling a bottomless vessel with water, which must be carried to it in sieves.

And even Tantalus, who had dared to feed the gods a meal of human flesh and had therefore been condemned to an everlasting agony of thirst and hunger, enjoyed a brief respite from his torment as the music of Orpheus reached his ears. Above Tantalus's head hung many varieties of fruit, ripe and delicious, and at his feet was the purest of waters, cool and refreshing to the throat. But he could have neither, for whenever he bent to drink the water would gurgle away, and no matter how quickly he might reach for the fruit, which seemed so close to him, it was always beyond his grasp. This everlasting agony of thirst and hunger was relieved for a few moments, however, as Orpheus's music performed its charms.

Finding himself in the presence of Hades and his pale queen, Persephone, Orpheus added golden words to the glorious strains of his lyre. "My wife Eurydice," he sang, "like all who lack the immortality of the gods, would some day have come to your realm, dread Hades. I too am destined at some time to submit to you. All I ask is that you allow her to return to the green earth, so that she might live out her allotted span of years."

Moved by his words, Hades relented. "Continue your music," he said, "and return from whence you came. Eurydice will follow you, for those melodies are enough to draw her away. But until you are on the earth again, dare not to look behind you!"

Orpheus was filled with hope, and, playing more beautifully

than ever before, he departed. Three-headed Cerberus, whose responsibility it was to prevent any from escaping, remained in his blissful stupor. And Charon, still hypnotized, gave passage once again across the River Styx.

And then the soul-wearying ascent began. The gloom of that winding tunnel was impenetrable. Sight was impossible, and only weary, stumbling feet provided guidance. The blackness was enough to overwhelm the soul, but Orpheus played on.

Great weights of time – you could not call them days – passed. Orpheus lapsed into a delirium. There was only one thing in his mind, and that was his hope that Eurydice followed.

Finally, the blackness resolved itself into grey, and Orpheus became aware that they were approaching the mouth of the cave. But his mind was tormented with doubts. Was it only he that had come so far? Eurydice – would she not have been walking more slowly, weakened as she was by the fatal snake-bite? Surely she was far behind. Perhaps she had fallen, and could not rise!

As sunlight streamed into the cave, Orpheus turned to see if Eurydice was behind him. He had looked too soon, however. She was there – Orpheus's music had indeed borne her upwards – but now she was slipping away. Orpheus clutched at her fading figure, but in his arms he held only air. A faint, whispered "Farewell" – and then she was lost again.

Now utterly forlorn, Orpheus wandered into the wilds of northern Greece, where Dionysus reigned supreme. There he proclaimed to all who would listen that his father, Apollo, was the greatest of all gods, and in the early morning Orpheus ascended a mountain to watch the returning sun conquer the night.

But it was dangerous to preach the greatness of Apollo and what he stood for – light, order, reason – in a land inhabited by the followers of Dionysus, and the maenads were sent to attack him.

When Orpheus saw the wild troop of women advancing towards him, he once again created the sounds that could enchant the keepers of the dead. The maenads hurled at him anything that they could lift – lumps of clay, rocks, the branches of trees. At first, charmed by the music, the missiles dropped before reaching their mark, but soon the insane yells of the women drowned out Orpheus's music, and he felt the sting of wounds. The creatures fell upon him, clawing at his body.

His head was cast into a near-by river, and as it was carried along towards the sea the sweet voice of Orpheus could still be heard. Finally it came to rest on the shores of Lesbos, where Apollo set up a shrine in his honour. The gods swore to punish the fierce maenads, but before the penalty could be exacted Dionysus transformed them into oaks, unable ever again to move from one spot.

HEROES OF
GREECE

A century ago, the stories of the Minotaur,
Medusa, and the Golden Fleece were regarded as mere fantasy. But in the interval
some of the most brilliant men of our times
– anthropologists, archaeologists, linguists,
classicists, historians, psychologists, philos-
ophers, and literary scholars – have probed
these tales in search of meaning; and now
we can state with some assurance what
elements of these stories are based on fantasy, what on actual events, and what on
ritual.

In 1900 Arthur Evans began to excavate
the ruins of a large building near Cnossus
in Crete, and he soon found reason for
naming it the Palace of Minos, after the
legendary king. The more he laid it bare,
the more it seemed like a labyrinth, for its
rooms were laid out in a truly maze-like
fashion. The sewers alone, large enough to
admit a man, could be regarded as the
Minotaur's Labyrinth. Even more striking
was a staircase (see the photograph on the
following page) that once climbed at least
five storeys – certainly, the architect who
designed it must have had the genius of a
Daedalus.

Everywhere in the palace were representations of the animal central to the Theseus
story, the bull. One painting showed three
youths apparently vaulting over the back
of a charging bull. Still more interesting is
the fact that two of the three participants
are girls. Could the seven girls and seven
boys of the Theseus story have been

brought to Crete to perform this dangerous ritual? The Minotaur, at any rate, is now considered to be the sacred king wearing the head of a bull, like the shaman of old. Thus, human sacrifice could well be the explanation for the fate of the fourteen.

The second photograph shows the domed inner room of a great tomb near Mycenae. The massive stone over the door weighs over a hundred tons, and the chamber within is made of blocks precisely laid to form a dome forty feet high. The bronze plating that once adorned this "bee-hive" dome has led some scholars to believe this to have been the bronze chamber of the Perseus story.

Not far from this tomb is Tiryns, where lived the king whom Hercules served. Though it was the mightiest of the Mycenaean strongholds, the Dorians eventually conquered it. The skeletons of its defenders were found at the foot of the walls.

Another place closely associated with these ancient stories has only recently been identified. This is Iolcus, the home of Jason, where successive settlements over thousands of years can be seen stacked one above the other like pancakes. Part way up can be seen the tell-tale charred wood of a Mycenaean palace, destroyed in the Dorian invasion. But these archaeological riches

Taurgo Slides

Taurgo Slides

will not be uncovered until the villagers who live atop the mound can be relocated.

Thus, all of these stories are rooted in actual places, and the main characters, though they could have figured in rituals, may well have been real people writ large. Their stories therefore seem more like legends than myths. They are *heroes*, not gods, and, like the arch-hero Gilgamesh, each resists the Mother Goddess.

10
THESEUS
AND THE
MINOTAUR

There are two unanswered questions about the Minoans, those creative people who established the great civilization of Crete: where did they come from? and where did they go?

A place of origin in Phoenicia is suggested by the story of Europa and the bull, and some scholars think that this was indeed the case. The griffin and the long women's dress, both found in Crete, are seen in Phoenician art as well; and the bull was revered throughout the Near East – witness the Bull of Heaven, the Golden Calf, and the cow-goddess Hathor. (Both Osiris and Horus were bull-gods – notice the tail that Narmer is wearing on page 22.) However, evidence that the Cretans wrote in the Greek language opens the possibility that the Minoan civilization had a northern origin.

The problem of the Minoans' ultimate fate is a more knotty one. Around 1500 B.C. the Palace of Minos was destroyed, and its inhabitants seem to have died or disappeared. It was once thought that a Mycenaean war-band, led by Theseus, had levelled the palace, but recent investigations near the island of Thera, seventy-five miles north of Crete, have provided a dramatic new explanation for these events. Around 1500 B.C. the island was blasted by an enormous volcanic eruption equal to the force of 450 hydrogen bombs. Within twenty minutes, waves up to 165 feet high hit the coast of Crete. This onslaught, and the poisonous fumes and hail of ash unleashed by the eruption, must have destroyed the Minoan civilization – not only on Crete, but also on Thera, two-thirds of which sank into the sea. The three days of darkness in Egypt before the Exodus may have been caused by the huge cloud of ash.

And an even greater mystery may now be solved. For in 1966 there was found, 1,300 feet under the water alongside Thera, a moat like that said to have been part of legendary Atlantis.

Europa

One day as she played in a meadow with her brothers, Europa, daughter of the King of Tyre, caught a glimpse of a great white bull grazing in a herd near the sea-shore. Though her brothers fled at the bull's approach, Europa was so dazzled by his beauty that she lost all fear of him. "How friendly he is!" she thought. "It's almost as if he were human."

He was not a mortal, however, but a god. Zeus had become enamoured of Europa, and to avoid troubling Hera he had taken the form of a bull.

As the white bull approached her, Europa placed flowers in his mouth, and, as she caressed him, the bull lowed gently. He rubbed his nose against the girl's elbow, as she garlanded his horns with flowers, and he bowed before her feet so that she might reach him more easily. His broad back looked so inviting that the girl could not resist the urge to climb onto it.

Scarcely had she done so, when the bull rose to his feet and ran towards the sea. At first this was exciting, as her laughing brothers ran alongside, but when the bull increased its pace they could no longer keep up with him and were left far behind.

Europa, crying out in vain to her brothers for help, held fast to the bull's neck. They plunged into the water, and the jolting gallop was replaced by powerful, smooth strokes as the bull swam serenely through the water. They were bound for the island of Crete. And there, in the mountain cave where Zeus had been born, Europa one day gave birth to a son, Minos. Minos became the Cretan king, and it was during his reign that Crete became a great civilization, called Minoan after the name of its great ruler.

Daedalus

The greatest craftsman of Crete was Daedalus. He invented the saw, using the jagged spine of a fish as his model, and the potter's wheel which he had devised was the forerunner of the most useful of all inventions, the true wheel. Daedalus was even said to have made statues that could walk.

But the most famous product of his fertile brain was the Labyrinth. The Labyrinth was a maze, the passage-ways of which were so intricate that anyone entering it would be unable to find his way out again. There was a reason for such a den – it was built to hide a terrible monster, the Minotaur.

The Minotaur had the body – the ugly, hairy body – of a man, but his shoulders bore the head of a bull. Its ravenous appetite only human flesh could satisfy. Victims were led into the Labyrinth, and as they groped about seeking an outlet the Minotaur had the pleasure of hunting them down.

Icarus

Daedalus, falling into disfavour with the king, was himself shut into the Labyrinth along with his son, Icarus. Too ingenious to be trapped for long, he found a passage-way out of the maze-like prison and then made plans to escape from the island of Crete.

He set to work to fashion two pairs of wings by joining feathers of different lengths and shaping them carefully with his deft fingers. When they were finished, he fastened them with soft bees-wax to his son's shoulders and to his own.

Then, in a stern voice, he said: "We shall fly to the north, over the sea. But take care! If you fly too near the sun, the wax on your wings will melt."

Like two great birds, they rose into the air, soared over Crete, then the sea and the islands of the Aegean. Icarus became more and more excited – how fast he could go! and how high! Intoxicated with the freedom of motion, he rose higher and higher.

Suddenly, Daedalus realized that the boy had not heeded his warnings and called to him frantically. But Icarus could not hear his voice, for he was only a speck far above his father. Then the speck began to grow bigger. Icarus's wings had fallen off and now he was plunging downwards. Daedalus caught but a momentary glimpse of his son's horror-stricken face as he fell past him towards the sea. A puff of spray on the water, and Icarus had drowned.

Aegeus

Minos had obtained a convenient source of food for the Minotaur. He had defeated the Athenians in war, and every nine years he demanded, in payment, seven youths and seven maidens.

Aegeus, the king of Athens, was troubled, not only by this curse upon his city, but also by the uncertainty of his own rule. In his court were many who could not be trusted – even his brothers were eager to assume the throne, and pass it on to their sons – and he knew that if he had any sons their lives would be in constant danger. For that reason, when he fell in love with the beautiful daughter of the king of Troezen, he married her secretly.

Before leaving Troezen to return to Athens, Aegeus said to his young wife: "If you should bear me a son, let him come to Athens only when he is full-grown."

"But how shall I know when the right time has come?" she asked.

"Look at this rock," said Aegeus, with a mighty heave raising a huge, flat stone. "When he is strong enough to lift it, he will be old enough to come to Athens. Tell him then that he is the son of Aegeus, and let him wear this sword and these sandals, which I now place beneath the stone. I will recognize them."

The Great Stone

A son was born, and his name was Theseus. He was a slim but muscular youth of fifteen when his mother led him for the first time to the rock. Theseus was surprised by his mother's order; nevertheless, he bent, and gripped the rock. He strained upwards until his young limbs quivered, but he could not move it. Panting heavily, he rested; and then, with a fierce burst of strength, he heaved at the rock. An inch it moved – but no more. He fought back tears of shame, and his mother said, "Let it be, son, for another year. By then you will be strong enough."

So Theseus waited one year, but into every day of that year he packed hours of exercise. He threw the discus, he raced (for his legs must be strong, as well as his arms), and, more than anything else, he wrestled. By the time he was sixteen, no man in Troezen could wrestle him for more than a minute without being thrown.

The day came, and Theseus again faced the great stone. He bared his shoulders, bronzed by the sun and rippling with layers of muscle. He selected his position, ground his feet firmly into the earth, and smiled confidently at his mother. Then, his back taut, his fingers tightened on the stone's rim, he fought his granite foe out of the earth in an explosion of energy. There before him, still intact, were the sandals and the gold-hilted sword.

Now Theseus's mother told him that his father was the king of Athens, and that the time had come to join him there. The hills of Athens could be seen in the distance, across the waters of the gulf.

"You should cross by ship," she said, "for the trip by land is full of dangers."

"No," he replied. "I have been given sandals, and I must walk." And, after bidding farewell, he set out along the coastal road.

The Trip to Athens

His route was indeed beset by perils, though he soon had another weapon of defence. First of all, a giant bearing a great iron-clad club attacked him, and Theseus instantly seized his foe's right arm and twisted it until the club fell from his grip and the giant crumpled to the ground. Theseus then picked up the massive club and used it to shatter the brigand's skull.

Continuing on his way, Theseus noticed torn pieces of clothing hanging from the tree-tops. When another, deceptively jovial, giant appeared before him, Theseus had already guessed what was coming. The giant wanted Theseus's help in bending a pine tree down to the ground. Help him he did, but when the top of the tree had been secured on the ground, Theseus knocked his friend out with his new club.

Then he gave the ruffian the same treatment that others had received at his hand. He tied the Pine-bender's head to the tree-top they had just pulled down, and, after wrestling another pine tree to the ground, attached his feet to that one. Then he released the two trees. Snap! Now there were two more strange objects swinging from the tree-tops.

When Theseus came to a narrow path high over the sea, he was stopped once again – this time by a huge man, dishevelled in appearance, sitting behind a basin of water.

"Before you may pass, you must pay your toll!" the man barked.

"What is the toll?" asked Theseus.

"Wash my feet," was the reply.

As Theseus cautiously got down on his knees to perform this unpleasant task, he peered over the edge of the cliff. There, at the water's edge, was a great man-eating turtle, its mouth gaping. Just as the Toll-collector was about to push him off the cliff, Theseus caught his leg, and toppled him over the edge. The turtle seemed to enjoy this meal, but it would have to wait a long time for another.

At Eleusis, Theseus encountered a powerful wrestler who insisted on trying his skill on every passer-by. Though the wrestler specialized in the bear-hug, this time he was to be the victim and not the victor, for Theseus crushed him until he heard the sound of cracking bones, then threw him lifeless to the ground.

As Theseus approached Athens, a man with a long beard rushed into his path and cried out in a friendly voice: "Good evening! I invite you to spend the night at my inn. I have a wonderful bed, which is sure to fit you. You may even have heard of the Bed of Procrustes?"

Fortunately, Theseus had indeed heard of it. This man was Procrustes, the inn-keeper who believed that each of his guests must fit his bed. If the bed were too short, it was no trouble to remove the visitor's feet, or even his head, if necessary. And, if the visitor were too short for the bed, he could easily be stretched to fit it.

But Theseus did not fancy having any such alterations made on himself. Instead, he threw his struggling host onto the bed, and, since Procrustes did not fit it properly, Theseus lopped off his feet and his head, just as the inn-keeper had done to so many others.

The Poisoned Cup

Now Theseus entered Athens, where further troubles awaited him. A witch, who had gained influence over Aegeus, knew that Theseus was approaching, and in her jealousy planned to kill him. She told Aegeus that he was shortly to be visited by an assassin, and prepared a cup of poisoned wine for him.

When Theseus arrived at the palace, he was filled with excitement at the prospect of seeing his father, and of being recognized. The old king came forward to welcome him – but his mind had been so filled with fears and suspicion that he did not know his own son. Looking into the young stranger's face, Aegeus sensed that there was something unusual about him. Convinced that this was the assassin, he offered him the fatal cup. Theseus accepted.

Suddenly, just as they were raising their cups to their lips, Aegeus caught sight of the gold-hilted sword. At once, he dashed the poisoned cup from his son's grasp, and, without speaking, embraced him.

Ariadne

Great as the rejoicing was over Theseus's arrival in Athens, an atmosphere of great gloom hung over the city, for the next payment to the Minotaur was due. Even now the unlucky victims were being chosen, and, to his father's dismay, Theseus volunteered to be one of the fourteen. The young men and maidens that had been selected were escorted to their ship by a lamenting crowd.

"I will return, Father," said Theseus. "I will kill the Minotaur, and there will be an end to this slaughter."

"Ah, you must return," said the grieving old man. "And when the ship returns, lower the black sail and raise the white one to tell me that you are still alive. I will be watching for it."

"I promise," said Theseus.

When the ship entered the Cretan harbour, throngs of colourfully clad people watched the Athenians disembark. Among the spectators was Ariadne, daughter of King Minos. At once, her eyes rested on Theseus – and she could not tear her gaze from him. What strength, what grace, what resolution! Her eyes drank in his broad shoulders, his full-chested torso tapering to muscular thighs. Ariadne stared, unbelieving, for she had not known that such men existed. Ariadne had fallen in love with Theseus.

As the Athenians were led to their cells, Ariadne trembled with fear. He must not die! To aid him would be to set herself against her father, but that is what her love demanded. That night Ariadne, her heart burning with ardour, sent for him.

Theseus was led into her chamber. Ariadne trembled at the sight of him, and she looked down until she was able to speak.

"I can help you," she whispered, handing him a ball of thread. "As you enter the Labyrinth, begin to unwind this. To find your way out, follow the thread back to the entrance. Now, quickly, hide this in your cloak." And she handed him a sword.

"You are truly a gift from the gods," said Theseus.

Ariadne looked up at Theseus's face, and their eyes met. "If I save your life," she said, "and help you to escape, will you take me back to Athens with you as your bride?" Moved by Ariadne's plea and enraptured by her beauty, Theseus readily agreed.

The Minotaur

That very night, the victims were led into the Labyrinth by its keepers, carrying lamps. Two dismal passage-ways opened, and they took the left one. A few yards along and a doorway opened on the right, but they passed it by. Then they took the middle fork of three and, after a short distance, a passage-way to the right. They continued to twist and turn, double and redouble, until the Athenians were completely bewildered. Only the guards knew the way back, and now they left the fourteen to their fate. As the keepers made their way to the entrance, they did not notice the thin thread.

The Athenians were now in total darkness. Whenever they

moved, their feet clattered against the bones of the Minotaur's victims. But they did not roam far, for Theseus had told them to stay together, and to move back when he attacked the Minotaur.

Suddenly, they sensed a sharp, heavy odour – the Minotaur was near. They heard the shuffling of brutish feet, the scraping of horns against the stone of narrow passages, and the loathsome sound of the Minotaur searching out his victims.

Theseus pushed his companions back and stood with sword in hand. The monster stumbled onwards and, though Theseus could see nothing, he knew that it had turned a corner and was directly in front of him.

With a grunt, the beast charged directly into Theseus's sword, which sliced through its neck. The Minotaur bellowed, uttered a fearful moan, and then a gasp of death.

The Return

Following the thread he had left behind, Theseus conducted the group back to the Labyrinth's entrance, where they were met by Ariadne. Through the dark streets she now led them, and on to their ship. With the utmost caution they slipped across the harbour, and then, raising their sails, they swept out over waters reddened by the dawn.

At length they arrived at the island of Naxos, where they disembarked to rest. Here Ariadne, dazed by love, wandered with Theseus until she yielded to exhaustion and fell into a deep sleep.

Towards evening, she awoke, and thought at once of Theseus. For a moment or two she lay looking up at the heavens, where violet clouds were massing in a yellow sky, and then she sprang up to see where he was. About her she saw only rocks and gaunt trees turning to silhouettes in the dimming light. She heard the distant thudding of the surf, and her eyes turned towards the sea. Far out on the grey waters, Ariadne saw the Athenian ship.

Theseus had left her behind. The hard shock of realization swept over her, and she began to weep bitterly. Then her soul filled with hatred, and she cried out to Zeus for vengeance.

Ariadne's prayer was granted. Theseus, his mind a turmoil of jarring emotions, forgot to raise the white sail as the ship entered the harbour of Athens. On the Acropolis, the rocky plateau where Athena's temple stood, King Aegeus had kept a constant vigil. For days he had scanned each approaching ship, seeking the one that was to bring his son back again, and now it was coming. He concentrated his aged vision upon it, unable to believe that he was seeing a black sail.

"Yes, it is black!" he suddenly cried. His life robbed of meaning, Aegeus staggered to the rim of the plateau and threw himself to his death.

The ship slid through the waves towards the harbour of Athens, where a large crowd was gathering. On the bow stood Theseus, straining to detect the father he had known for such a short while. Soon he was close enough to make out every face lining the wharf – and it was only then that he remembered.

It was too late to raise the white sail, for already the ship was nearing the wharf. One by one the youths and maidens stepped ashore, into the arms of loved ones weeping for joy at their return, but no Aegeus was there to greet Theseus.

When Theseus learned of his father's suicide, he was overcome with grief and remorse. And, before becoming King of Athens, he set up a shrine in his father's name.

shrine

11
PERSEUS
AND MEDUSA

Several of the incidents in the Perseus story may seem like elements of folklore. The visit to the Grey Hags, for instance, is almost certainly a folk-tale. And the encounter with Medusa may recall the fairy-tale theme of the witch in the candy house. But Medusa means "queen", and we may take this as a clue to her existence in myth rather than in folk-tale, for she is probably another form of the Mother Goddess. It has been suggested that her priestesses may have worn hideous masks to scare away those not permitted to witness their ceremonies.

So Perseus's slaying of Medusa (see the accompanying photograph of a sculpture in the ruggedly simple Archaic style) may signify the overthrow of the Mother Goddess's shrine. The same may be said of Apollo's conquest of Python, for serpents are almost always associated with Mother Earth. An actual historical example of such an overthrow concerns a religion in Ethiopia which featured the regular sacrifice of kings: in the third century B.C. a reformer simply marched his soldiers into the temple, killed every priest, and instituted his own religion. It is significant that Andromeda was in Ethiopia, not far from the land of the Shilluk, who sacrificed maidens along with their sacred kings. Perhaps Perseus's slaying of the dragon and rescue of Andromeda refer to the suppression of a similar cult.

Thus the Perseus story is probably a legend – an exaggerated account of actual events. And Perseus is a *hero* – a real, though somewhat glorified, human being. (One archaeologist is so confident of Perseus's past existence that he lists him as a king of Mycenae, *circa* 1350 B.C.) Nevertheless, his adventures follow the pattern established by the god-kings of myth: insecure youth, death-struggle with a monster, Sacred Marriage, and kingly rule. His triumph is given added lustre by his rescue of a damsel in distress.

Taurgo Slides

Danae

"You will be slain by your own grandson."

As he travelled homeward from Delphi, this was the prophecy that Acrisius, King of Argos, was pondering. Determined to prevent the fulfilment of this terrible prediction, he decided to follow the only course of action possible – he had no grandsons now, and none must ever be born!

Acrisius had one daughter, Danae, a most beautiful maiden. To prevent her from marrying, he ordered the construction of a chamber, plated with bronze, and here the girl was imprisoned. A strong defence – but what armour is there against fate?

One day, as Danae sat by a window, she saw a distant shimmering in the sky. As it came closer, she could see that it was a shower of gold flakes. The shining cluster rushed through the window and, with a crash of thunder, took the form of a god. It was Zeus.

A son, Perseus, was born to Danae. When Acrisius learned that the dreaded grandson had been born, he was filled with consternation, yet he could not bring himself to kill the infant in cold blood. Instead, he had the young mother and her child locked into a wooden chest and set adrift.

In the blackness of that flimsy chest, Danae was numb with terror. From the calm bay into which it had been launched, the chest drifted into the unprotected sea. Danae, clutching her son, felt the great waves dashing against the thin wood of their craft, making it slide sickeningly down, then up, then down again. For long hours the churning swells flung them about, draining them of all strength and feeling.

So weak did mother and child become, that they could hardly sense the change as the chest was carried into gentler waters, into waves that only lapped at its sides and eventually nudged it towards land. When Danae felt the grinding of wood against sand, she knew that they had come ashore, but she still lacked the strength to pry off the heavy lid of the chest. And there they would have perished, had not a fisherman found them.

It was on the island of Seriphos that Danae and Perseus had landed, and here they remained for many years, cared for by the fisherman who had rescued them. Perseus soon showed that he had not been harmed by his terrible experience. On the contrary, it seemed to have made him fearless, for at an early age he began to go out in the fishing boats, and no matter how violent the sea became he never felt the slightest timidity. The older Perseus grew, the more daring he became. In his youth, when his well-formed body was infused with manly strength, he established himself as the best athlete on the island. No challenge, whether it involved swords, spears, or fists, was too great for Perseus.

Polydectes

As for Danae, each year added new allure to her loveliness. One day Polydectes, the king of Seriphos, saw her. At once, he fell in love with her and determined to become her husband. But Danae, whose lover had been Zeus, the king of the gods, could take no interest in a mortal who ruled over one island, and she would have nothing to do with him.

Polydectes, however, was not daunted by Danae's attitude, and he resolved to marry her by force. There was only one serious obstacle in his way, and that was her dare-devil son. But there was a way of dealing with him.

Polydectes held a great feast, to which he invited Perseus and all the wealthy noblemen of the island. All but Perseus brought costly gifts. As each man stepped up to the throne and presented his gift, Polydectes took it in his hands and lavished excessive praise upon it. He deliberately left Perseus to the end, by which time the gleaming presents were piled high around the throne.

Perseus was fully aware that this sly king intended to humiliate him, and his face was red, more with anger than with shame. "No gift, Perseus?" said Polydectes, a cruel smile snaking across his lips. "Perhaps you are poor. But there is something that you could have brought, and it would have cost you nothing." He paused, and the smile fixed itself on his lips. "Why don't you bring me Medusa's head, Perseus?"

Perseus stared defiantly at the king and, in a cold fury, answered, "I will!"

The answer to this was uproarious laughter, for Medusa was one of three Gorgons, loathsome winged creatures with snakes for hair. Their faces were so horrible that the sight of them would turn any creature to stone, and anyone foolish enough to seek Medusa's head would pay with his life.

Perseus strode from the palace, out of earshot of the crowd. Now, for the first time, he thought soberly about his mission. Far away the Gorgons lived and it would take a long time to reach them. But when he finally did approach them, how could he avoid being seen, and attacked, by at least one of the monsters? And should he actually get the head of Medusa, what would he do with it? For one unwary glance at it would turn him to stone. Even cutting it off was a formidable task, since her neck was armoured with scales as hard as sea-shells. Finally, there was the seeming impossibility of killing something without looking at it. Perhaps, for once, Perseus's daring had surpassed his reason.

Suddenly, Perseus heard a whirring sound above him, and he looked up to see Hermes floating down from the sky, borne by his winged cap and sandals. With him was Athena, wearing her helmet of bronze. Within minutes, Perseus learned that two of his greatest problems were solved, for Hermes had brought him a magic sword, capable of severing Medusa's neck, and from Athena he had received a highly polished shield. Now Perseus could safely strike at Medusa, for by watching her reflection in the shield, he could avoid a fatal glance into her eyes.

Perseus was now wildly excited about his mission. Three problems remained, but Athena and Hermes knew how they could be overcome. To reach the distant island of the Gorgons, he would have to obtain winged sandals like those of Hermes. To prevent the Gorgons from spying him, a Helmet of Invisibility would be required. And to hold that terrible head Perseus would need a special wallet.

All of these things, Perseus was told, could be obtained from the sea-nymphs. The difficulty was that nobody knew where they lived – except the three Grey Hags.

The Grey Hags

These unfortunate creatures had been old ever since they were born. And there was only one eye between the three of them. Each had a socket, but whenever one wanted to see something, she had to grab the eye from the one who was using it, and clasp it into her socket. Since the Grey Hags would not give out any information of their own accord, the only way of extracting it from them was to snatch their eye and return it only when they had co-operated.

Perseus, following the directions provided by his friends, made his way to the gloomy land where the Grey Hags lived. He arrived just as they were having a bitter argument over the possession of the eye. It was an easy thing for Perseus to reach out and seize the eye, and as soon as he did the screaming and fighting became fierce.

"How dare you take it!" screeched the one from whom he had grasped the eye. "Give it back!" And she clutched at the nearest Hag – for she had no idea that Perseus had taken it.

"Get your hands off me! I haven't had the eye all day," the other snarled, slapping her accuser with a horny claw.

"You've got it, you've got it!" the first Hag squeaked, as she groped for the third. Finding a shank of hair, she pulled her sister's head towards her and felt in the socket for the eye.

"I have your eye," said Perseus. "And you won't get it back until you tell me what I must know."

Suddenly the Hags became pathetic, begging him to return their eye. Perseus did so, but only after he had received the information he had been seeking. As soon as he had returned the eye, the Hags started wrangling over it again, and by the time one had finally pushed it into her socket Perseus had vanished.

Medusa

Perseus soon found the sea-nymphs, and they did not hesitate to provide him with the sandals, wallet, and helmet he required. With mounting excitement, Perseus laced on the magic sandals. Suddenly, he felt his body lose its weight and shoot into the air – he was in flight!

High over sea and land Perseus soared at a dizzying speed. It seemed only minutes until he had arrived at an island strewn with strangely-shaped rocks. At once he realized that these were the Gorgons' victims, transformed into statues. And then he could see, in his shield-mirror, the monsters themselves.

Hideous they were in sleep, with their eyes open still, staring glassily ahead. The serpents, growing from their skulls, slept also, and hung like beards about the Gorgons' necks, though the whole tangle continued to seethe and hiss. From the Gorgons' mouths grew curving tusks and pointed teeth partially hidden by purple tongues as wide as shovel-blades.

Perseus descended until he was within inches of Medusa's head. The Gorgons showed no sign of alarm, however, for the Helmet of Invisibility prevented that. Then he struck. The magic sword bit into the vile neck, and through, and Perseus reached into the bed of snakes to grip the head. In an instant, he had dropped it into the wallet.

Then an astonishing thing happened. From the cavity in Medusa's trunk where her neck had been, two hooves burst forth, and then the head and body of a horse! From its mane grew a mighty pair of wings; they beat, and the horse – Pegasus – rose into the air.

Andromeda

Again the magic sandals thrust Perseus skyward, and carried him towards Seriphos. But his arrival at that island was to be delayed, for as he flew over the coast of Ethiopia he looked down and saw what appeared to be an ivory statue amid the rocks of the shore. He descended to observe it more closely, and just then a breeze blew, revealing a length of hair growing from the white form. It was a girl – an enchantingly beautiful girl – and she was chained to a rock.

Perseus landed beside her, and removed his Helmet of Invisibility. The girl was startled to see him suddenly materialize, but Perseus spoke soothingly, and she began to tell him her story. She was the Princess Andromeda, and to prevent Poseidon from causing a flood she was being offered as a sacrifice. Her explanation was interrupted by the appearance of a huge sea-serpent, slashing through the waves with its heavy breast.

Perseus wasted no time. He projected himself into the air between the sun and the serpent. The creature threw himself upon the shadow, and instantly Perseus plunged to the attack. Into the serpent's shoulder he sank his sword. Roaring aloud, the monster lashed out with ragged jaws, trying to seize its tormentor. But Perseus avoided its lunges and drove home the magic sword again and again. Soon the water was a bloody froth, and Perseus, fearing that his winged sandals would become drenched, leapt onto a rock. From here he delivered deadly blows – enough to drain the serpent of its remaining strength.

Now Perseus returned to Andromeda and severed her chains. The girl, weakened by terror, collapsed against his chest. He took her in his arms and carried her gently to the palace where she lived. By the time he had reached it, Perseus's heart was pounding painfully – but not from exertion. He had fallen in love with this exquisitely lovely girl.

In the palace Perseus found Andromeda's parents, suffering agonies of grief. Imagine their feelings when they saw their daughter, and learned of the sea-serpent's demise! There was, it was true, a price to be paid – but an easy one. Perseus asked for their consent to marry Andromeda, and never was parental blessing given so willingly.

After the wedding, Perseus proceeded to Seriphos with his young bride – and with his gift for Polydectes. When they arrived,

Perseus went alone to the palace, where the king was feasting with the same crowd that had mocked the young hero earlier. As Perseus stood in the doorway, Polydectes looked up and saw him.

"Ah, Perseus!" he cried. "Tell me, did you bring along my present?" He laughed viciously, and his friends hooted and jeered.

Perseus held up the head of Medusa.

Swiftly the colour on the men's faces changed from pink to grey – the grey of stone. Some, who had been standing when they saw the face, became too heavy to stand, and they toppled over, breaking into fragments. The faces of many were frozen at the moment when terror had begun to spread across their features. But Polydectes had been laughing so heartily that his stone lips were still parted in merriment.

Acrisius

Perseus, even after the supreme adventure he had just experienced, was still eager to participate in athletic contests, and he took part in a festival of games on the island. He performed magnificently – but particularly in the discus. Compressing his body into a muscular spring, he released it with perfect grace, propelling the discus farther than it had ever been thrown before.

Again and again Perseus sent the discus spinning past the eyes of admiring spectators. Then a freakish current of wind deflected the heavy missile into the crowd. It struck and instantly killed a white-haired old man.

As the people clustered helplessly around the old man's body, someone cried out, "Why, this is Acrisius!"

When Perseus heard this, he could not believe it. "But Acrisius is King of Argos," he exclaimed.

"He was," came the reply. "But for fear that some oracle might be fulfilled, he came to Seriphos."

Acrisius was dead, and now Perseus became king in his stead.

12
THE
LABOURS
OF HERCULES

We shall probably never know whether a Hercules ever existed. Scholars regard his name as that of a man, not a god, but his miraculously rapid growth places him alongside Marduk, Apollo, and Hermes – and, of course, he was in due time actually elevated to the ranks of the gods. Others believe that his name ("renowned of Hera") refers to his original status as the consort of Hera, the ancient Mother Goddess, and that it was only later on, when the Indo-Europeans, worshippers of male gods, appeared in Greece, that he was thought of as being opposed to her.

Whatever the case, it seems clear that to the original story of Hercules dozens of additional tales (only a few of which are included in this book) were appended, and many of these take the form of myths. There are several incidents in these stories that refer to rituals in which a king was involved, and some of Hercules' deeds, such as those in which the capture of animals was required, have been interpreted as tasks set for those seeking the kingship.

In his fight with Achelous, for example, Hercules succeeds in breaking off one of his opponent's horns. We are reminded here of Theseus's victory over the Minotaur – the king in his bull-mask overthrown by his young rival – and of Enkidu, who grasped the horns of the Bull of Heaven before slaying him. Bulls' horns, regarded from early times as sources of supernatural power, were probably symbols of kingly rule. (Consider the mace held by the English monarch of today.)

Another ritual connected with the kingship is that in which the king, or in later times an image of him, was burned on a hill-top. At Mount Oeta, the very mountain on which Hercules is said to have been cremated, ancient inscriptions describing the burning of statues of the king have been found.

Youth

Two huge snakes, their scales glistening a light blue colour, and poison oozing from their fangs, slid towards the cradle. The baby boy within awoke to see them hovering over him, eyes glinting, heads poised for the kill. With a gurgle, he reached out and grasped their necks. As his small hands tightened on the blue scales, the snakes writhed and jerked, coiling and uncoiling their sinewy bodies. But they could not escape. Bouncing and laughing in his cradle, the boy held fast until his playmates' lashings subsided and their bodies became limp ropes. Hercules, a mere eight months old, had killed them.

Surely such a child must have had remarkable parents. The mother of Hercules was Alcmene, granddaughter of Perseus. When her husband had been banished to Thebes, she had accompanied him there, and that is where Hercules' exploit was later to take place.

Once, her husband left to fight with the Theban army, and, while he was away, Zeus, his appearance and voice altered so that he resembled her husband perfectly, visited her, telling her that the war had ended. So it was that Zeus became the father of Hercules.

Alcmene, amazed by the strangling of the snakes, asked Tiresias, the blind wise man of Thebes, what this event could mean. "He is to be the strongest of all men!" was the reply. "He will do great deeds for mankind." And as soon as Hercules had matured he proved Tiresias's prediction true, for in addition to his enormous strength he had a deadly aim, and with his bow he rid the country of many troublesome beasts.

Hercules was magnificent in appearance – seven feet tall, with a frame to match, and eyes that flashed fire. On one occasion, when he was tracking down a lion in the vicinity of Mount Helicon, a king welcomed him to his palace at the base of the mountain. This king had fifty beautiful daughters. They were so pleased to have Hercules staying at their palace that he was distracted temporarily from his hunting. They took turns in waiting on him, each daughter having been given a day to herself, so that it took him fifty days to catch the lion.

The deed which established Hercules' supremacy, however, was his defeat, almost single-handedly, of a country which had forced Thebes to pay it tribute. In gratitude, the Theban king gave his daughter to Hercules in marriage, and appointed him the city's protector.

For several years Hercules enjoyed complete happiness with his family, but, as you may imagine, Hera harboured ill feelings against Hercules. It was she, in fact, who had sent the snakes to destroy him. Now she struck again, and this time took her vengeance indeed.

Madness

One day, as Hercules sat watching his sons playing, the sky overhead suddenly darkened and a terrible change came over him. Staring wildly about and foaming at the mouth, he grasped his bow and rose to his feet.

He began shooting arrows at his own sons, and, within seconds, all had been fatally wounded. When their mother appeared, summoned by their shrieks of pain, Hercules again loosed an arrow, and again it struck home.

Hera had driven him mad, and, in a moment of derangement, he had slain his entire family.

As soon as the slaughter was over, Hercules regained his sanity and endured the heaviest torment of remorse. Now almost mad with grief, he went to Delphi to ask how he might atone for his crime. This was the priestess's reply: "Go to Tiryns. Serve King Eurystheus. For twelve years you will perform labours. In reward, you will be granted immortality." And thus it was that Hercules undertook his famous twelve labours.

The Nemean Lion

The first labour that Eurystheus imposed on Hercules was to kill the lion of Nemea. This seemed like an almost impossible task, since no weapons could pierce its skin. He solved this problem by first knocking the beast senseless with one stroke of his massive club, and then throttling it. His task performed, he carried the lion on his back to Tiryns, although Eurystheus, startled by the sight, told him to deposit his catch outside the city walls in the future.

Hercules put the lion's body to good use, however. The pelt, he thought, would provide an excellent protective covering, if only it could be cut loose – for no metal or stone could so much as scratch it. Then he was struck by an idea.

Gripping one of the paws, he bent the lion's leg back so far that he could rake the skin with its claws. The lion's own claws, he found, could pierce the skin, and by drawing the claws across it Hercules was able to cut it away from the flesh. Now he had fashioned himself a fine suit of armour, for the impenetrable hide of the beast neatly covered most of his body, allowing him to peer out through its gaping jaws.

The Lernean Hydra

Lerna, a foul swamp by the sea near Tiryns, was the dwelling-place of the Hydra, a monster with nine heads, one of which was immortal. Hercules, ordered by King Eurystheus to destroy the Hydra, had armed himself with his bow and arrows, his club, and a sword. When he found that the arrows and club made no impression on the Hydra, he slashed at it furiously with his sword. Whenever he had sliced off one head, however, two sprouted in its place, and, to make matters worse, an enormous crab appeared that tried to lop off Hercules' feet with its pincers.

Soon, however, he had solved his difficulties. With flaming branches he seared the wound left by each head as it was removed, to prevent them from growing back. Then he dealt with the crab by crushing it. Finally, he chopped off the Hydra's immortal head and partially silenced its hissings by burying it under a rock.

Again Hercules found a use for his victim's remains. In the Hydra's intestines was a quantity of poisonous gall. By dipping his arrows in it, Hercules ensured that a wound from them would mean certain death to any of his foes.

The Cernean Deer

The third labour imposed on Hercules was the capture of a deer with golden antlers, which roamed the woods near Cernea. Since Eurystheus wanted him to bring the animal back alive, Hercules brought it down by shooting an arrow neatly through the fore-legs, pinning them together. He had sent the arrow between the bone and the muscle, so that no blood was spilt. Artemis, to whom the deer belonged, was angry, but Hercules placed the blame for the deed on Eurystheus.

The Erymanthian Boar

A huge boar was ravaging cattle on Mount Erymanthus, and again Hercules was required to capture it alive. This posed no problem, however. He merely chased the boar through heavy snow-drifts until it collapsed with exhaustion, and then bound the beast in chains.

The Augean Stables

King Augeas, who ruled near Olympia, had an unpleasant problem to contend with. His barn, in which he kept three thousand cows, had not been cleaned out for thirty years; so Eurystheus sent Hercules over to undertake the task. Hercules looked the situation over and then made Augeas an offer. "Promise me one-tenth of the cattle, and I'll do the job before nightfall." The king, laughing scornfully, agreed readily to this seemingly impossible proposal.

Hercules began by knocking out two sections of the stable wall, one at each end. Then, starting at the upper end of the barn, he proceeded to dig trenches in the direction of two rivers flowing swiftly through the farm. When he reached them, the waters rushed down the trenches, through one end of the barn and out the other. When the dung accumulated over thirty years had all been washed away, Hercules plugged the trenches and the task was done.

Now Augeas tried to back out of the agreement by claiming that Hercules was already under orders to Eurystheus. Hercules, annoyed at being slighted, slew him and, with the riches of his kingdom, established the Festival of Games at Olympia.

The Olympian Games were to be held every four years in honour of Hercules' father, Zeus. They were to last for five days, and for a month afterwards all wars between Greek states were to cease. Hercules himself paced off the Olympian stadium, making it 600 feet long. And, to provide a shady spot in the valley at Olympia, he planted olive trees, decreeing that victors in the games should be crowned with their leaves.

The Stymphalian Birds

The sixth labour he undertook was the destruction of the man-eating Stymphalian birds, creatures with brazen beaks and feathers. These birds shot their sharp, metallic feathers at men and then swept down to eat their bodies. Hercules killed as many as he could with his poison-tipped arrows, but, finding them too numerous to exterminate in this way, frightened the rest away by shaking a great bronze rattle.

The Cretan Bull

The first six of Hercules' labours had been carried out near Tiryns, but the remaining six were to be performed in more remote places. For his seventh task, he went to Crete to capture a wild bull which had gone mad and was ravaging the crops and walls of the island. Hercules caught the beast and carried it back to Eurystheus.

The Thracian Horses

As his eighth labour, Hercules was ordered to travel to Thrace and there capture some wild horses. The owner of these horses usually gave them the flesh of his dinner-guests for food. The animals were uncontrollable until Hercules gave them something else to eat – their master; whereupon, completely tamed, they accompanied Hercules to Tiryns.

The Queen of the Amazons

The Amazons were a race of women who had gained control over their husbands. To ensure their continued superiority, they broke the arms and legs of all boys born to them, so that they would never be good for anything but household chores. Thus the women had time for what they most enjoyed – fighting.

Hippolyta, the Queen of the Amazons, possessed a marvellous girdle, made of finest gold, which Hercules was sent to obtain. The Amazons lived south of the Black Sea, and he had to make a long and difficult journey to get there. When he arrived, Hippolyta welcomed him into the palace and seemed quite willing to make him a gift of her beautiful garment.

Hera, however, brought trouble to Hercules once again. Disguised as an Amazon, she went about spreading the rumour that Hercules intended to carry off, not only the girdle, but their queen as well. Thus, while he was talking with Hippolyta, the Amazons leapt on to their horses and attacked.

Hercules, believing that Hippolyta had ordered this treachery, killed her instantly and removed her golden girdle. Then, picking up his bow, he sprayed arrows into the on-rushing Amazons, breaking their charge and enabling him to escape.

Geryon's Cattle

Geryon, one of the strongest creatures alive, had three different bodies, joined together at the waist. On the island of Cadiz off the coast of Spain he kept a herd of beautiful red cattle, which Hercules was to steal.

Arriving at Gibraltar after many adventures, Hercules set up two huge pillars, one on each side of the straits. Then he proceeded to Cadiz. For the trip across to the island, Hercules was given an enormous golden goblet shaped like a water-lily. When he set out, using his lion-skin as a sail, the Titan Oceanus, whose waters he was now disturbing, began to rock the goblet menacingly. Hercules in turn threatened Oceanus with his bow, and the sea became calm.

Landing on the island, Hercules was met immediately by Geryon. Since each of the creature's three bodies was well covered with armour, Hercules had to aim well – he shot each of them squarely in the eye, and one by one they fell limp, until all were on the ground in a heap.

Now remained the problem of getting the cattle back to Greece. Hercules herded them into the giant goblet and took them to the mainland. From then on, the trip was overland – a distance of two thousand miles. His progress was unimpeded until he entered northern Greece, where Hera had sent a huge gadfly to stampede the herd in all directions. With great difficulty Hercules rounded up all the cows, however, and brought them to Eurystheus.

The Golden Apples

Hera's wedding gift from Gaia had been a tree bearing golden apples. Hercules' eleventh labour was to obtain these apples, although he had no idea where they could be. There was one person, however, who was certain to know – Prometheus, the Titan. And, in order to give his son yet another measure of fame, Zeus now permitted him to put Prometheus's tortures at an end.

Hercules arrived at the Caucasus Mountains just as the great eagle was descending to feast again upon Prometheus's liver. A single shaft from Hercules' bow and the torture was over. He took Prometheus's rusted fetters in his hands, and snapped them.

"The great Zeus, my father, has sent me to release you," Hercules said. "But now you must help me. Tell me where I can find the golden apples given to Hera at her wedding."

Prometheus opened his mouth to speak, but after centuries of silence could at first make no reply. Then, after drinking the water offered by his liberator, he replied: "Go to the mountain on which my brother Atlas stands to support the sky. On its slope Hera has planted the tree, and she has appointed the maidens called the Hesperides to guard it. Ask Atlas to help you."

Hercules once more journeyed westwards, for the mountain of Atlas rises to the south of Gibraltar. There he found the Titan, stooped under his incredible burden, and he asked him to fetch the apples.

"Why yes, I think that can be arranged," replied Atlas. "Only take this weight from my shoulder for a few moments while I gather them for you."

Hercules went to Atlas's side and bent to receive the weight. With a grunt Atlas transferred the sky to Hercules' back, gave a sigh of pleasure, and strode down to the garden of the Hesperides. After five minutes, even the great Hercules was finding the sky an oppressive burden. "What a weight!" he thought. "I hope Atlas doesn't take much longer. If I remain like this for long, I'm sure my spine will snap."

Then, just as he was about to call out to Atlas to return, apples or no apples, he saw the Titan coming back up the mountain, whistling happily and tossing the apples from hand to hand.

"Here are your apples," he said light-heartedly. "The Hesperides were asleep. But, now that I've done a favour for you, I'm going to take a little holiday and deliver the apples."

Hercules did not like the sound of this. He suspected that Atlas, when he had tasted some more freedom, would conveniently forget all about his substitute. Furthermore, he simply could not bear the agony any longer. "All right, Atlas," he replied. "You've done me a good turn. But I'm not very comfortable. Do you think that you could show me a better grip?"

"So, you find that burden somewhat heavy, do you?" laughed Atlas. "Let me show you how the job is done!"

He bent down beside Hercules and took the sky once again. "You were doing it the wrong way," he said, as Hercules reached down to pick up the apples. "You had all the weight in the middle of your back. Look at me, now – I have it further up, almost on my shoulders. And see how I'm using my arms."

But Hercules was not watching. He was already on his way back to Tiryns.

Cerberus

The twelfth and final labour was the capture of Cerberus, the three-headed watchdog of Hades. This would be the most hazardous task of all, for to do it he would have to descend into dread Tartarus.

The entrance that he used was the cave in Mount Taenarum through which Orpheus had also travelled. Following the winding, dank tunnel downwards, he came at length to the River Styx. Here, the boatman Charon was about to stop him, but a menacing scowl from Hercules persuaded him otherwise.

He was ferried to the other side, and there he met his shaggy, three-jawed foe. Another fierce glower from Hercules, and Cerberus shrank back, whimpering.

Now he was in the land of the dead, and he could see the ghosts scurrying away as he approached. One creature stood firm, however, and with a start Hercules realized that he was staring at Medusa! But now she was only a phantom and he was unharmed.

In the gloomiest depths of Tartarus, he found Hades and made his request. "You may take him with you," replied Hades, "but you must use neither your club nor your arrows."

Hercules now returned to the River Styx, where the watchdog waited for him, barking with all three heads and thrashing the air with his tail. To subdue Cerberus without using weapons, Hercules lifted the animal from the ground and proceeded to squeeze some of the life from it. When its snapping, slobbering jaws sought to tear at his flesh, they met only the impenetrable hide of the lion-skin; and when the animal began to choke, Hercules lifted it to his shoulders, took it across the Styx on Charon's boat, and then carried it back to the entrance to the cave, and thence to Eurystheus.

Arriving at the king's palace, Hercules let his quarry loose, crying, "There it is! My last labour is over!"

Eurystheus, terrified by Cerberus, who had now revived and was rushing about barking fiercely, cried out, "Take it back to the Underworld!" And thus it was that Hercules returned Cerberus to his old post.

Deianeira

Now that the murders committed by Hercules during his madness had been atoned for, he wished to settle down and remarry. And, during a visit to the King of Calydon, Hercules fell in love with his beautiful daughter, Deianeira.

Deianeira already had a wooer named Achelous, whom she did not care for. Achelous had the body of a serpent, the face of a man, and the horns of a bull, and water flowed incessantly from his immense beard.

Achelous, after hurling insults at Hercules, challenged him to a wrestling-match. He proved a rather slippery opponent, however, and as soon as Hercules had pinned him to the ground, he turned himself entirely into a serpent and slithered away.

Then he turned himself into a bull and attempted to gore his opponent. But Hercules was waiting for him, and, seizing one of Achelous's horns, he threw him to the ground so violently that the horn was broken off. This was enough to daunt Achelous, who surrendered his claims to Deianeira. Hercules married the girl forthwith.

Nessus

Deianeira loved Hercules greatly, but, since he continued to visit other lands to perform heroic deeds, she became jealous of him and wished to ensure that no one else would win his heart. An opportunity to gain this security came about in a strange way.

Once, while on a journey with Deianeira, Hercules came to a flooded river. Just as he was about to carry his wife across on his back, the centaur Nessus appeared – a horse with a man's chest, head, and arms. He offered, for a price, to carry Deianeira across the stream while Hercules swam the distance. The agreement was made, and they set out.

But Nessus, entranced by Deianeira's beauty, decided to run away with her, and Hercules looked up to see him clamber up the far bank and then gallop off into the distance. Again Hercules had to display good marksmanship. Still in mid stream, he fitted an arrow to his bow and shot at Nessus just as he was vanishing from sight. His aim was perfect, and Nessus stumbled to the ground.

The centaur, even in his dying moments, planned his revenge. He told Deianeira, "If you wish to prevent your husband from falling in love with any other woman, take some of my blood and smear it on his shirt." The foolish girl believed him and collected some of the blood that flowed from the centaur's wound. She did not know, however, that mixed with Nessus' blood was the poison of the Hydra, into which the fatal arrow had long ago been dipped.

The time came when Deianeira had cause to use this dreadful substance. Hercules had gained a great victory over a town to the north, and a beautiful princess was reported to be among the captives. Preparing to raise an altar and do sacrifice to Zeus, he sent for a special garment that he wore on such occasions. Deianeira dipped a piece of wool into Nessus' blood, and applied it to the garment.

When the messenger had taken the shirt to Hercules, Deianeira sat, considering what she had done. Suddenly, she saw smoke rising from the knot of wool she had been using. The smoke flared into flames, and within seconds the wool had turned to ashes. Horrified, Deianeira dispatched another messenger to overtake the first, but she was too late.

Hercules had received the garment and had put it on, for it was time for the sacrifice to begin. Twelve oxen were slaughtered, and then other animals – a hundred in all. They were laid on the high-piled wood, a torch was applied, and the flame bit into the wood-sap and consumed the slain beasts.

Now Hercules began to sweat from the intense heat, and, as the garment clung to his body, the poisoned blood of Nessus began to eat into his flesh.

Pain assaulted his body; he gave a frightful cry and tore at the treacherous shirt. The flesh came with it, however, revealing the bones beneath. He threw himself into a stream, but the poison consumed him all the more. Then, in extremest agony, he stumbled about, tearing up trees by the roots. Spying the messenger who had brought the fatal shirt, he grasped him by the ankle, whirled him around his head, and threw him against a rock.

But soon Hercules' strength began to ebb, and he gave his soldiers these instructions: "Carry me to this mountain-top. Prepare another pyre of wood, and place my body upon it."

His orders having been carried out, Hercules lay down upon his lion-pelt, his head resting upon his club. Suddenly, thunderbolts descended, and the pyre was reduced to ashes. Zeus, in Olympus, had proclaimed that his son's mortal part had been burned away – to be replaced by another, an immortal body, just as the Oracle of Delphi had foretold. A cloud shrouded the mountain top, and the great hero was carried up to the home of the gods in a chariot drawn by four horses; there he lived forever, serving as guardian of the gates of Olympus.

13
JASON
AND THE
GOLDEN FLEECE

The Jason story is an excellent example of how myth, legend, and folk-tale can become entwined. It contains elements highly suggestive of sacred ritual that probably have their basis in myth: the combination of serpent, tree, and girl; the husbandless women of Lemnos, who like the Amazons seem to date from a time when the Mother Goddess was dominant; the task that Aeetes assigns Jason, which closely resembles the ritual tests undertaken by candidates for the kingship; and the story of Phrixus, which is set on a mountain-top and involves the near-sacrifice of a son and the substitution of a ram for the child.

Surprisingly enough, a similar ritual is still performed annually

British Museum

a mountain near to that on which Phrixus was to have been sacrificed. Every May Day, men wearing white fleeces go through the motions of killing, and then bringing back to life, an old man wearing a black-sheep mask. Medea's dealings with Pelias are also suggested by this ceremony. (The vase painting on the preceding page shows Medea rejuvenating a ram.)

The explanation for this May Day ritual seems clear. At one time, the sacred king was sacrificed on a mountain-top. Later, a substitute for him was slain – a boy, probably clad in a ram's fleece. And, finally, only a ram was sacrificed. As the Biblical story also does, this ritual emphasizes the point that human sacrifice is no longer called for.

All of the elements mentioned above seem to be mythical illustrations of rituals. Others have their basis in folk-tale. In one version of the Jason story, for instance, Medea slows down her pursuers by flinging fragments of her brother's body behind her – the "magic flight" theme of folklore.

And then there is the voyage of the *Argo*, which is probably legendary in origin. In early times voyages into the Black Sea were undoubtedly made by men searching for precious metals and other goods. The Golden Fleece, for example, may have been nothing more than a sheep-skin placed in the river-bed for the collection of gold-dust. And, since a shipyard is still in operation today not far from Iolcus, where the *Argo* is supposed to have been built, it is quite likely that the same trade flourished there in ancient times.

Pelias

"Beware of the man with one sandal!" This was the warning given to Pelias, King of Iolcus, by an oracle.

In his old age, Pelias had seized the throne from his brother Aeson. He did not feel secure in his reign, however, for he could not bring himself to execute his brother, and he was troubled also by the oracle's prophecy.

Pelias became even more alarmed when he learned that the wife of Aeson was about to give birth to a child, and he resolved to have it slain. But, just after a son had been born to the woman, her serving-women set up a wail of mourning. It was announced that the child had died, and within a few days a small coffin had been buried.

Many years later, in the midst of a great festival, a report reached Pelias that a young man of striking appearance had arrived in the market-place. And, to the old man's alarm, he saw a tall, broad-shouldered youth with long hair, shod only with one sandal, advancing towards him with two spears in his grasp.

Pelias shuddered with fear, for he sensed that the prophecy was being fulfilled. "Who are you?" he asked.

"I am Jason, son of Aeson," said the youth.

The child that had been mourned had not died. Instead, he had been smuggled out of the city and raised in secrecy. Now he was ready to assume power, and delivered his challenge: "I have come to regain the throne, which is my father's!"

Pelias knew that resistance would be unwise and he therefore replied: "That may be. But there is one thing you first must do. The ghost of Phrixus bids us bring back the Golden Fleece. Perform this task, and I shall yield up the throne."

"I will do it!" said Jason.

Phrixus

What was the Golden Fleece, and who was Phrixus? That is a story in itself.

Phrixus, when still a boy, had been the victim of a cruel plot devised by his jealous stepmother. First, she had contrived in secret to ruin the year's seed by roasting it over the fire, so that the crops would fail. Then, when her husband had sent to Delphi for advice, she had bribed the messenger to give him this false message: "Only if you offer up your son as a sacrifice will the land become fertile."

So Phrixus was led by his bitterly weeping father to the assigned place of sacrifice, a mountain-top. With a supreme effort of will, the father laid his hand on his son's shoulder, and raised his knife.

Suddenly, a magnificent winged ram with golden fleece swooped down from the heavens and landed beside them. In an instant, Phrixus was on the ram's back, its wings clapped together, and the boy was borne skyward.

High in the air they flew, over the scattered isles of the sparkling Aegean, and over steel-grey mountains to the Black Sea. On its eastern shores, at Colchis, they came to earth again. Here, Phrixus offered up the golden ram as a sacrifice to Zeus, and hung its fleece in a grove, guarded by a dragon that never slept.

The Argonauts

For the voyage to Colchis, Jason assembled the greatest band of heroes that had ever been seen. Among them were Calais and Zetes, winged sons of the North Wind; Orpheus, who at this time had not met Eurydice; and, along with his armour-bearer, Hylas, the mighty Hercules, who at this time had just completed his fourth labour. Since their ship was called the *Argo*, these warrior-sailors, fifty in all, were known as the Argonauts.

They had to contend with two difficulties before they could even embark, for at the farewell banquet quarrels broke out among some who had partaken of the wine too heartily. But Orpheus calmed them with the sweet strains of his lyre.

Then, when launching-time came, the *Argo*, heavily laden with provisions, refused to budge. Once again, Orpheus saved the day, and, charmed by his music, the *Argo* glided down the sand to the sea.

Lemnos

Lemnos was their first stop. The men of this island had all been murdered by their wives. When the *Argo* approached, a hostile army of women, clad in their husbands' armour, swarmed down to the shore to fend off a feared invasion. But, when they saw the noble bearing of the Argonauts and learned that their intentions were peaceful, they permitted a landing and offered the men gifts of food and wine.

So greatly did their attitude towards the men change that they would gladly have had their visitors remain. They even offered Jason the kingship. Hercules was eager to be on the way, however, and, urged by him, they departed.

Hylas

When the wind slackened, Hercules challenged the others to a contest to see who could row the longest. After many hours of toil, all but Jason and Hercules had dropped out. They were still rowing their hardest, when Jason fainted from exhaustion and, at the same time, Hercules' oar snapped in half. Hercules was furious, for the mishap prevented him from claiming the victory.

When they landed that evening, Hercules went into the woods

to find a tree from which he could fashion a new oar. He came back, dragging a sturdy pine, to learn that Hylas, his young armour-bearer, had not returned after going out to look for water. Throwing the tree to the ground, Hercules crashed bull-like into the woods, roaring Hylas's name. But, though he came upon the abandoned jug, he never did find Hylas, for a water-nymph, charmed by the boy's appearance, had drawn him down into the depths of her spring.

The next morning the Argonauts, taking advantage of a fine breeze, set sail. Now there were only forty-eight, for Hercules had stayed behind to continue his futile search before returning sorrowfully to Greece to resume his labours.

The Harpies

Phineus, the ruler of eastern Thrace, had once foretold the future too accurately for Zeus's liking and had been punished, as a result, with blindness and the visits of two Harpies. These foul creatures, with the wings and claws of birds and the bodies of women, swooped down to Phineus's dinner table at every meal, snatching the food from his hands and even from his mouth, and imparting a loathsome odour to what remained.

When the Argonauts landed, Phineus, now an old man with wrinkled, papery skin, tottered out to meet them. "We have two in our number who will rid you of the cursed Harpies," Jason told him, in return for the promise of helpful advice.

At a banquet prepared especially for the visitors, the opportunity came. A horrid flapping and loathsome penetrating odour announced the arrival of the Harpies. Calais and Zetes, swords in hand, flew up at them and began a pursuit that took them far into the distance, never to return. This left only forty-six Argonauts.

The Symplegades

The Argonauts were sorry to lose the winged brothers, but, as a result of their work, they received vital information. Grateful Phineus told Jason how to get through the Symplegades, which guarded the entrance to the Black Sea. They were known as the Clashing Rocks, for whenever a living creature ventured between them they would sweep together and crush it.

Setting sail the next day, the Argonauts soon heard the dull crashing of the rocks and the thunder of rushing surf. Then they rounded a bend and beheld an awesome sight, for the rocks were opening up only a short distance before them. Now was the time to act.

As Phineus had instructed him to do, Jason released a dove. As it passed through the opening, the rocks moved together again. There was a ringing, resounding collision, and a great surge of water swept against the *Argo*, but, when the rocks separated again, the dove could be seen flying on ahead, leaving only a few of its tail feathers behind.

Heaving mightily on their oars, the Argonauts now sped into the opening, just as the rocks gathered themselves for another on-slaught. A foaming wave that shot out from the base of each rock at the *Argo* only served to push the ship through before the rocks ground together again with a deafening roar. The stern ornament was torn off, but otherwise the ship remained intact.

The Symplegades moved apart again, never more to collide, for it had been decreed that, if ever one group of men succeeded in getting through, the rocks would thenceforth become immobile.

Aeetes

From Mount Olympus, Hera and Athena were watching with intense interest the exploits of their favourite mortal, Jason. They knew that the King of Colchis, Aeetes, would not readily allow him to take the Golden Fleece. Thus, they decided that Medea, the king's bewitching daughter, should be persuaded to help Jason. The first step was to make her fall in love with him, and for this purpose they sought the aid of the love-goddess herself. Aphrodite agreed to do her best.

Aphrodite had a son called Cupid. She approached him as he was shooting dice with a friend (and cheating him), and asked him to fire an arrow of love into Medea's heart. When he had been bribed with the offer of a new toy, Cupid rose from Olympus and flew towards Colchis.

By this time, Jason had arrived at the same place and had entered the palace of King Aeetes. At first the Argonauts were treated to warm baths and a banquet – but when Jason had revealed the purpose of his visit, Aeetes became rigid with rage.

"Leave!" he shouted. "Leave my kingdom before I have your

tongues torn out and your hands lopped off! You seek no fleece, but the throne and realm of Colchis!"

But Jason made a soothing reply, assuring the king that he had but one aim – to obtain the Golden Fleece; and Aeetes changed his tone.

"Let us first see", he said, "if you are worthy of so great a prize as the Golden Fleece. Two bulls I have, with hooves of bronze and breath of fire. In the span of one day I yoked these bulls, ploughed the field of Ares, and sowed the furrows with a dragon's teeth. From these teeth armed warriors sprang up, and I killed them all! Only if you can do as well have you a right to the Golden Fleece."

Jason was at first speechless, but, gathering his courage, he replied: "Necessity impels me to accept your terms."

Medea

Harsh terms they were, and Jason might well have been doomed had it not been for the activities of Cupid. He had just arrived, and as soon as he spied Medea he let fly an arrow. As she stood watching Jason pronounce these words, the shaft entered her heart, right up to the feathers.

Medea, now suffering the extremest agonies of love, gazed at him with troubled heart. She knew at once that she would have to choose between loyalty to her father and love for Jason – for Medea possessed a magic ointment which, if smeared on the hero's body, would protect him from the blows of the bronze hooves and from the searing flames which issued from the mouths of the bulls.

In the night, Medea was afflicted by dreams in which Jason seemed to have come to carry her off as his bride, and she awoke, determined to offer him aid. Four times Medea tried to go to him, and four times feelings of guilt prevented her. The ache of Cupid's wound and the realization of her disloyalty brought her close to committing suicide. She picked up a casket of poisons. The dread of death struck her, and then a vision of the delights of life. She put away the poisons, took up the magic ointment, and went to Jason.

When she found him, she was at first powerless to speak, for her eyes were held captive by the sight of him. Tenderly, she placed the magic ointment in his hands and told him how he should proceed on the morrow.

"When you go away, remember me – remember that I saved your life," she whispered, "for never shall I cease to think of you!"

From the first, Jason had been dazzled by the witch-maiden's beauty, but now his heart had melted. "You shall come with me to Iolcus," he said, "to live there as my wife."

The Brazen Bulls

At dawn, Jason faced the bulls. Bracing his legs and holding high his shield, he awaited the onslaught. With hooves gleaming and nostrils breathing forth streams of fire, the beasts flew at him. The shock of collision did not move Jason, nor did the flames singe his body, for Medea's charms did their work.

Grasping the bulls by their horns, Jason brought them to their knees, and harnessed them to the yoke by brute force. Their bronze hooves dug into the earth, the plough jerked forward, and, as great waves of soil were flung aside, Jason sowed the dragon's teeth.

Instantly, the gleam of metal appeared in the earth, helmets shot up, and a host of warriors rose into view, each one turning on Jason as if he were his enemy. But Jason picked up a stone and threw it into their midst as Medea had instructed him. Each soldier thought that the man next to him had thrown it, and they set upon one another like hounds. Jason himself strode amongst them, reaping the crop with his sword.

When the soldiers had slain one another and the furrows of the field were red with blood, Jason went to the king, asking him to honour his promise. "Tomorrow," jealous Aeetes muttered – but even as he spoke he made plans to massacre the Argonauts and burn their ship.

Fearing the worst, Medea slipped from the palace under cover of night and hurried towards the Argo. "Leave at once," she warned the sailors, "for my father is plotting some treachery! Row to the grove of the Golden Fleece and I myself will render the dragon harmless."

The Golden Fleece

In the stillness of the night, the heroes pushed the *Argo* from the shore and began rowing once again. Medea was troubled at betraying her father, but Jason soothed her with words of love, swearing that when they came to Iolcus he would make her his wife.

The *Argo* ground onto the shore at the place where Phrixus had sacrificed the ram. Jason and Medea set out on a path into the murky woods. Suddenly, amidst the blackness of trunks and leaves, there shone a cloud of shimmering gold – it was the Golden Fleece. And beside it glowed the green spheres of the dragon's eyes. The dragon roused itself and reared up into the air, its numberless coils made visible by the radiant beauty of the Fleece.

Then Medea began to sing softly, and gradually its fierce head could be seen to grow heavy, droop, and finally sink to the ground in slumber. Medea sprinkled her most magical potion upon its eyes and the dragon was caught in the web of sleep. Quickly Jason took the Golden Fleece from the branch where it hung. But even now a whisper of light was appearing in the east. Jason and Medea hurried back to the *Argo*, and the rowers pulled the ship away from the shore.

Apsyrtus

By now, Aeetes knew of the Argonauts' flight, and of his daughter's disappearance. He summoned the populace to the market-place and ordered every able-bodied man to join in pursuit. Soon the massive Colchian fleet, commanded by Apsyrtus, the king's son, was sweeping over the sea like a flock of birds.

The Argonauts, eager to see their homeland again, were straining mightily at the oars. But before long they saw a sail on the horizon – Apsyrtus's flagship, manned by the strongest of the Colchians, was gaining on the travel-weary Argonauts. Orpheus encouraged them with vibrant strains on his lyre, but, when they put ashore that night, Apsyrtus's camp was not far distant.

Now Medea plotted against her brother. She sent him a message stating falsely that she had been carried off against her will and calling upon him to rescue her. At the designated meeting-place, Jason would be waiting in ambush.

Apsyrtus unsuspectingly walked into the trap, and Jason sprang upon him with his sword. Medea looked away so that she might not see the slaughter of her brother, but drops of his blood fell upon her dress. Thrice Jason tasted of his victim's blood and thrice he spat it out to prevent the ghost from haunting him.

The rest of the Argonauts seized the opportunity to attack the leaderless crew. Like a forest fire they raged through the Colchian camp, sparing no one. Then they resumed their journey, having shaken off their pursuers.

Pelias

Finally, one evening in the fall, the triumphant Argonauts beached their vessel at Iolcus. Here Jason received the sad news that his parents had been put to death by Pelias.

Medea was the instrument of revenge. She went alone to Pelias's house, crying out that Artemis had come to reward the king for his piety, and she promised the daughters of Pelias that she could make their old father young again. To convince them, Medea demonstrated her powers on an aged ram.

First, she prepared her potent brew in a large cauldron. Into it she threw magic herbs and minerals, the flesh and wings of a screech-owl, the entrails of a wolf, a water snake's scaly skin, a stag's liver, the head of a crow, and a thousand other ingredients. Medea stirred the frothing liquid. Where drops fell to the ground, the flowers and grass of spring sprang up.

Then the witch-maiden drained the ram's blood, carved its body into thirteen pieces, and flung them into the cauldron. She sang her charms. Suddenly, a bleating was heard, and out leapt a young lamb!

The daughters were convinced. While Pelias slept, they gathered around his bed. Medea had instructed them to cut up their father and drain his blood. At first they hesitated, but with a great effort of will they began their fearful enterprise. Their courage having failed them, Medea completed the deed by slitting the old man's throat and plunging his mangled body into the cauldron.

Now the king's daughters waited to hear Medea speak her magic charms. But she had vanished, and never would Pelias emerge from the boiling cauldron, either old or young.

Medea had run to the palace roof to signal to Jason that he could now lead his Argonauts into Iolcus, and become king.

ΒΑΣΙΛΕΟΣΕΛΘΟΝ

HEROES OF THE TROJAN WAR

One day in 1829, a seven-year-old boy saw a picture of the walls of Troy. When he asked his father if the walls were still standing, he was told that they did not exist and that those in the picture were only the artist's invention. Then and there the boy, named Heinrich Schliemann, vowed to find them.

Forty-one years later Schliemann, now a millionaire, set a gang of men to work digging at a great mound in north-eastern Turkey, which he thought contained the city of Troy. And, as it soon became evident, he was right. Actually, he uncovered nine cities, each built on the rubble of the previous one. In the second and third layers from the bottom, Schliemann discovered great walls and unmistakable evidence of fire. Surely, he thought, this was the ravaged Troy of Priam and Hector, for their city was burnt to the ground.

After three years of excavation, Schliemann had decided to go no further. Then, on June 15, 1873, *one day* before he had planned to leave, he struck gold. Beneath the massive walls of what he believed to be Priam's palace gleamed the royal treasure. When Schliemann had adorned his lovely Greek wife with the diadem, earrings, and necklace which he found, he beheld in his fevered imagination a Helen born again.

This was not Priam's treasure, however, and later excavations showed that the jew-

Taurgo Slides

ellery, and the palace under which it had been found, were a thousand years older than Priam. But there was one settlement – level VIIa – which is believed to have been destroyed by fire around 1250 B.C., the traditional date for the Trojan War. (It is likely, by the way, that such a war was fought, since Troy controlled the trade route into the Black Sea.)

Schliemann's greatest triumph was yet to come. In 1876 he began digging at Mycenae, the city of Agamemnon. He was guided by Pausanias's words about the area just inside the walls and behind the famous Lion Gate, where "Agamemnon lies and those who were murdered with him".

In short order Schliemann made his first discovery – a "grave circle" of upright stone slabs (right), within which he found nine other slabs. Down he dug, through stony rubble which by luck had been washed down from above, thus preserving the area

Taurgo Slides

from robbers. Soon he reached solid rock and then the edge of a shaft cut into the rock – the first "shaft grave" of Mycenae.

Four shaft graves he found, each filled with gold implements of the finest workmanship, and then a fifth, the most exciting of all. For here the bodies of three men were found, the faces of each covered by awesome gold masks. As the masks of the first two were removed, the skulls beneath crumbled to powder. But, as Schliemann gently lifted the mask of the third man (left), he saw the teeth, the flesh, the eyes of an ancient warrior. This, he wildly believed, must be the face of Agamemnon.

But again Schliemann's dates were wrong. The occupants of the first grave circle had lived some four hundred years before the date usually given for the Trojan War, and the burial place of Agamemnon is more likely to have been the great bee-hive tomb shown on page 77.

14
THE
WRATH
OF ACHILLES

It was the Mycenaeans who won the Trojan War. But within a century of their victory they were themselves defeated by the Dorians, who spread destruction across all of Greece. A large group of Mycenaeans seem to have crossed the Aegean Sea during this period and settled in eastern Asia Minor, and with them came the minstrels who had sung the stories of their wars.

Centuries passed and styles of warfare changed. The hurling of boulders and spears became obsolete, and soldiers wielding swords now attacked in orderly ranks. The Mycenaeans' weapons had been made of bronze; but the Dorians' were formed of iron; the bulky body-shields of the type worn by Ajax were replaced by round shields like Hector's. Burial gave way to cremation. But the minstrels continued to sing poems in which the old ways were described, though with these they combined passages dealing with later practices. Then, around the eighth century B.C., a great poet emerged who drew upon the songs of centuries to produce two poems called the *Iliad* and the *Odyssey*. His name was Homer.

The *Iliad* describes only the tenth year of the Trojan War, up to the funeral of Hector. And, because of its detailed treatment of the quarrel between Achilles and Agamemnon, it bears the subtitle, "The Wrath of Achilles". The voyage of Odysseus, described in the next chapter, is the subject of the *Odyssey*.

The *Iliad* and the *Odyssey* are epics – long poems describing the adventures of heroes. The legend of Gilgamesh was the first of the great epics, but in vividness of detail and clarity of organization Homer's epics far surpassed their Babylonian model. Indeed, they have never been equalled in magnificence. For the young Greek warrior these epics were an education in heroism, for they gave him communion with men who displayed true nobility.

The Apple of Discord

Once, Zeus fell in love with Thetis, a beautiful sea-goddess who lived in the coral caves of the ocean. His mind was inflamed by her loveliness, and he wooed her incessantly even though Poseidon became his bitter rival, and even though Hera harassed him and Thetis herself resisted his advances.

One day, however, he suddenly broke off his courtship, for Themis, the mother of Prometheus, had warned him, "If the sea-goddess gives birth to a son, he will surely be greater than his father!"

That was enough for Zeus, and his hopes for a marriage with Thetis vanished. "So this was the marriage-match the fire-stealer knew of!" he said to himself. It was a close call, and for a while longer he would be able to avoid the fate of Cronus and Uranus.

When Thetis married, Zeus made sure that her husband was a mortal man. He was Peleus, a stalwart warrior, one of those who had voyaged with Jason in his quest of the Golden Fleece. But his son was to be far greater than he, just as Themis had foretold, for the child to whom Thetis gave birth was Achilles, who was destined to be the finest warrior of all time.

The wedding of Peleus and Thetis was attended by all the Olympians, and afterwards the gods enjoyed a great feast. Hephaestus went hobbling amongst them, ladling nectar and ambrosia from his serving-bowl, and Apollo raised his golden voice in song – though he could hardly be heard above the chatter of the goddesses.

Eris, the twin sister of Ares, had not been invited to this banquet – and with good reason, for her name means Discord. Nevertheless, she came. Suddenly flinging open the door, she rolled into the the midst of the gathering a golden apple, and, with a screech of laughter, vanished. Inscribed on the apple were the words, "For the Fairest".

Zeus stepped forward to pick up the apple, and you may imagine his consternation when he read the inscribed words. As the husband of Hera, he felt obliged to award it to her, the Queen of Olympus. But how would proud Athena feel about such a choice? And who would be more likely to complain than Aphrodite, who was the goddess of beauty?

Zeus decided to stay out of harm's way. He ordered Hermes to conduct the three goddesses to Mount Ida, near Troy, where the matter would be decided by a beauty contest. The judge was to be Paris, son of King Priam of Troy. Paris was of all men the most handsome – and thus well qualified to judge the beauty of women.

Soon Paris, who was tending the herds on the mountain slopes, saw Hermes approaching with the three beautiful Immortals, and he shrank back in fear and amazement. Then Hermes handed him the apple and the young prince read the inscription.

Hera was the first to step forward. She turned slowly so that Paris could fully appreciate her tall, regal beauty, and addressed him: "Obviously, the apple is meant for me. And for you I intend great power. Choose me, and you shall be ruler of all Asia."

Athena, wearing her helmet of gleaming bronze, was the next to approach Paris. "What power is there", she asked, "but that of the mind? If I am chosen, I will give you supreme wisdom."

And, finally, Aphrodite stood before him. She paused for a moment before speaking, a radiant smile upon her face, and then whispered, "If you give me the apple, I will win for you the loveliest of mortal women."

Aphrodite held out her shapely hand and, dazed by her beauty, Paris dropped the apple into her palm. Hera and Athena glared angrily at them, then strode away. Discord had begun among the gods.

Helen

The most beautiful woman in the world was Helen of Sparta. There was only one difficulty in Aphrodite's plans – Helen was already married.

The selection of a husband for Helen had been a problem, for every prince in Greece had hoped to have the loveliest of women for his wife. Even at the age of twelve she had been extraordinarily beautiful and at that time the great Theseus had tried, without success, to claim her as his bride. When she came of age the danger still remained that her rejected suitors might unite to do violence to the fortunate man chosen to be her husband. Therefore, each of her suitors was required to swear an oath to bring to punishment anyone who tried to steal Helen away from her husband.

Helen could have chosen one of the heroes as her husband: the mighty warrior Diomedes, who was desperately in love with her; the brave but foolhardy Ajax, a giant among men; the cleverest of all men, Odysseus; and the man who was to become the greatest hero of them all, Achilles. But her decision fell to red-haired Mene-laus, who was the richest of her suitors.

Now Aphrodite had the task of making Helen available for Paris. Her first step was to have him come to Sparta, where he was welcomed heartily by Menelaus, the Spartan king, and his lovely wife. But so taken was Helen with the strength and beauty of the Trojan's presence, that she could say almost nothing. Aphrodite now employed all her wiles to assist Paris in winning Helen's heart.

For a time, Paris merely gazed in rapture on her perfect face, but gradually he grew bolder. Lifting her goblet to his lips, he drank from the side that her lips had touched. And then he traced on the table before her very eyes the words "I love you."

Menelaus suspected nothing and, after a few days, he departed on a hunting trip, asking Helen to entertain their guest in his absence. The power of Aphrodite was irresistible. As soon as Menelaus had left, Paris and Helen, deliriously in love, stole away to Troy.

Upon his return, Menelaus was told of his wife's elopement. Enraged, he declared that the Trojan's act was an insult to all Greece and demanded that the severest punishment be exacted. Troy must be attacked!

Those who had been the suitors of Helen were now summoned to fulfil their oaths. Many were reluctant to do so, but eventually a thousand ships were manned, which sailed first to an assembly place at Aulis.

The commander-in-chief of the Greek forces was Agamemnon, the brother of Menelaus, who had married Helen's sister, Clytemnestra. Nobody knew then that Clytemnestra, like her beauteous sister, would some day betray her husband, or that Agamemnon would, in time, suffer even greater misfortune than had Menelaus.

The Youth of Achilles

By the time the Greeks had gathered to sail for Troy, Achilles had already grown to manhood. His teacher, the wise centaur, Chiron, had raised him on a diet of wild honey, the entrails of lions, and the marrow of fawns, a diet that gave the boy such speed that he was able to outrun stags.

His mother, Thetis, had taken great pains with his upbringing. She had even sought to make him immortal. When Achilles was only a baby, she carried him down to Tartarus and, holding him by one heel, dipped him head first into the River Styx. Wherever he had been touched by those terrible waters, he thereby became immune from harm.

Now, learning that the Greeks were anxious to have her son recruited for their war-force, Thetis dressed him as a girl and sent him to a palace where many young girls lived.

The Greeks delegated the wily Odysseus to seek out Achilles. Disguised as a pedlar, he came one day to the palace and unrolled his pack. As he displayed his goods, the girls gathered around, giving cries of pleasure as each trinket was revealed. One of them, a rather large girl, seemed to take little interest, however, and stood back as the others reached out to claim the rings, bracelets, and jewels that caught their fancy. Then Odysseus drew forth a jewelled sword. The one who had taken no notice now sprang forward, grasped the sword, and swung it in the air. Achilles had been exposed.

The Quarrel

With Achilles added to their ranks, the Greeks set sail for Troy. The prows of a thousand ships sliced across the Aegean, and at length the Greeks landed on the shores of the plain where stood the citadel of Troy.

But their hopes for an early victory were soon dashed, for the Trojans refused to come out and engage in decisive combat with them. And, since the Greeks had no siege weapons, a blockade of the Trojan citadel was the best they could do. The Trojans were not suffering, however. Water was in good supply, and by making quick raids on the enemy's positions they were able to break the blockade and bring in food. It was a stalemate – a stalemate that was to endure for nine long years.

The Greeks replenished their supplies by taking town after town in the vicinity. On one of these raids, Achilles captured a beautiful maiden, Chryseis, whom he presented to Agamemnon as a gift. Chryseis's father came to the Greek camp, pleading for her release, but the commander-in-chief angrily sent him away. But the father of Chryseis was one of Apollo's priests, and the archer-god was not long in answering his servant's plea for vengeance.

Apollo began to rain fiery arrows upon the Greek camp. Day and night, the twang of his silver bow could be heard, and fires burned continually to consume the dead.

Soon, Agamemnon was persuaded to send Chryseis back to her father. What he demanded was almost enough to guarantee defeat for the Greeks. He resolved to take another maiden, Briseis, to replace the girl he had given up.

Briseis belonged to Achilles, however, and when Achilles learned of Agamemnon's intention, he was ready to draw his sword and run him through. Only the intervention of Athena prevented him from doing so. Instead, he snarled at his leader: "Dog-faced, doe-hearted drunkard! You will regret this! The time will come when Greeks will fall by the hundreds to man-slaying Hector. Try to stop him then, for I will not!"

And so Achilles withdrew from the warfare. Agamemnon would indeed have reason to regret his move. Achilles, in the sporadic fighting of the first nine years, had proven himself the most valiant of the Greeks. Now there would be no one to match the magnificent Trojan – Hector, son of Priam.

When the soldiers had taken Briseis away, Achilles was plunged into misery. Thetis heard him, and rushed to his side. "Mother," he exclaimed, "you are loved by Zeus. Go to him now, clasp his knees, and implore him to side with the Trojans. Let the Greeks be slaughtered. Let them be flung back to the ships! Then their commander will know what a fool he has been to have offended me."

Paris and Menelaus

Thetis did her son's bidding, and within moments she had arrived at Zeus's side. When she spoke, the great god bowed his immortal head in agreement. After considering how best he might carry out her wishes, he decided to mislead Agamemnon in a dream.

"Call your troops to arms, advance, and take the city of your enemies!" Agamemnon was told. "Troy is yours!"

The next day Agamemnon, inspired by this false promise, led forth his gleaming forces. The Trojans, having learned that the mightiest of the Greeks was sulking in his tent, then streamed out onto the plain as well, ready at last for combat.

It seemed that Zeus's plan would go into operation immediately, but, just as the armies were about to clash, Paris stepped forth from the ranks and challenged any of the Greeks to fight him man to man. Menelaus, the husband of Helen, strode forward.

When Paris saw that his worst enemy had taken up his challenge, he lost heart and jumped back into the ranks. But Hector cast scornful words in his brother's face, and Paris, fighting back his cowardice, put on his armour. A truce was declared and it was decided that the possession of Helen would be decided by the duel.

On a measured piece of ground, Helen's two lovers took up their positions. Paris was the first to hurl his spear – it failed to pierce Menelaus's stout shield. But Paris was not so lucky, for Menelaus's spear crashed through the Trojan's round shield and tore into the side of his tunic, just grazing the flesh. In a flash, the red-haired Greek seized the horse-hair plume of Paris's helmet, and began to haul his choking victim towards the Greek lines.

Aphrodite had not forgotten Paris and the golden apple, however. She had been looking on, and now, with one deft movement, she severed the chin strap of Paris's helmet. Menelaus fell over backwards, clutching an empty helmet in his hands. Recovering himself quickly, he made another rush at Paris – but his foe had disappeared! Aphrodite had carried her favorite off and deposited him in Helen's perfumed bed-chamber.

Diomedes

Aphrodite was by no means the only Olympian to interfere on the battlefield, for Athena had not forgotten the beauty contest either. The proud goddess was all for having the Greeks slaughter the Trojans, and she chose mighty Diomedes as her great champion.

First, Athena arranged to have the Trojans break the truce, by inspiring one of them to shoot an arrow at Menelaus. The shaft wounded him but slightly, for Athena had deflected it, but Diomedes was not long in exacting revenge – his spear, guided by Athena, killed the villain instantly.

Now the armies finally swept into battle, their glistening helmets like the crests of ocean waves hurtling down upon the beach. And raging everywhere was the wild Diomedes – like a lion among cattle, he slashed at the men of Troy.

Aphrodite was soon forced to make another appearance, for Aeneas, who was her son, was wounded by Diomedes. As Aeneas bestrode the body of a slain friend, protecting it against any seeking to strip it of its armour, Diomedes lifted an enormous rock and sent it crashing down on Aeneas's hip. He fell to his knees and lost consciousness. Diomedes would have finished him off had not Aphrodite descended to shield him with her lovely arms.

Diomedes, however, cared not that a goddess sought to protect one of his targets. He loosed a spear at her. The point went home, and wounded that exquisite flesh. The blood of the gods flowed, and Aphrodite fled, screaming.

Apollo, he whose priest the Greeks had offended, replaced the love-goddess. But even he could inspire no fear in Diomedes' heart. Four times he threw himself against Apollo's shield, struggling to get at Aeneas. Finally, the archer-god shouted at him in his rage, "Do not think, Diomedes, to be the equal of the gods!" At these words, Diomedes stepped back, and Apollo was able to carry off Aeneas's wounded body.

Next to oppose Diomedes was Ares, the god of war himself. Diomedes was dismayed, but Athena cried out, "Do not fear this madman! Strike him down!" Then she leapt into Diomedes' chariot and drove the horses directly at Ares. Spattered with gore, the war-god let fly a spear, but Athena deflected it out of the way. Then Diomedes sent his spear whistling towards him, which Athena guided straight into his belly. Bellowing as loudly as ten thousand soldiers, Ares flew up to Zeus like a whirlwind.

Hector and Andromache

While Diomedes was thus occupied on the battlefield, striking out at men and gods, great Hector was in Troy hunting for Paris. He found him in Helen's room, inspecting his armour and weapons.

"Why do you sulk here," said Hector, "when men are giving up their lives for your rash deed?"

Helen joined in: "How I wish that I had a better man than this one. He cares not that everyone holds him in contempt."

"Just get him out on the battlefield again," said Hector, "before the Greeks put the torch to our city!"

Hector left the unhappy pair and went to see his wife, Andromache, once more, before returning to the battle. She saw him approach and ran to meet him, followed by a nurse carrying their baby son.

As tears rose to her eyes, Andromache put her hand in his. "Hector," she said, "do not join in the battle today. Stay with me here behind the walls. You know that my father and my seven brothers are all dead, slain by terrible Achilles. I have no mother. You, Hector, are father and mother and brother to me. Do not leave me!"

"I cannot hide myself like a coward," Hector replied. "Always

I have trained myself to fight in the front ranks, to find glory for my father and myself. Andromache, I know that Troy will fall! But far better to die than to hear your cries as they drag you off to captivity."

Hector reached out to embrace his child. But the boy, frightened by the great bronze helmet and the horse-hair crest nodding above it, shrank back to his nurse's breast. His father and mother laughed at the sight. Then Hector removed his glittering helmet; he kissed his son, and tossed him in his arms. "O Zeus," he cried. "Let this boy some day rule Troy! May it be said of him, 'He was greater than his father'."

He handed the child to his wife. When he saw Andromache smiling through her tears, he caressed her tenderly and said, "You must not be troubled about me. Hades will not claim me before my time. But do not hope to escape the workings of Fate. Go home now while I return to the battlefield."

The Retreat to the Ships

The first day of battle ended, and Zeus had not yet carried out the requests of Thetis. The Greeks had not been pushed back to their ships; instead, it was the Trojans who had been sent reeling. But now Zeus took control and addressed the Olympian gods. "None of you must help either the Trojans or the Greeks!" he boomed. "I have my plans, and no one is to interfere with them!" With that, he dashed off to Mount Ida, which overlooked the Trojan plain.

Zeus surveyed the battlefield, considering how he might conduct the fighting with the greatest amount of bloodshed. He decided to give the Greeks the advantage for a while longer, before throwing them back to the shore. He therefore sent Hector this message: "Agamemnon will be allowed to advance in the morning. But keep an eye on him, for as soon as he is struck by a spear you are to attack."

So the next day, when Agamemnon led his forces onto the battlefield, the Trojans immediately fell back before the Greek assault. The Greeks swept across the field like a wind-driven forest fire, and by noon the Trojans had been forced back half-way across the plain, intent only on finding refuge behind the city walls.

Then it was Hector's turn. Seeing a spear strike Agamemnon's forearm and pass right through it, he shouted: "Attack now, you Trojans! Look! We have hit their leader, and now Zeus will give us the victory!" Then, like a sudden squall, he fell upon the Greeks.

Within minutes, the Greeks began to give way. But Diomedes was not to be shaken; instead, he raised his spear and flung it at the oncoming Hector. Fortunately for Hector, his helmet was thick! He heard the loud clang as bronze met bronze, and his senses were momentarily dazed.

But Diomedes was not able to press his advantage further. Paris, who had finally reappeared on the battlefield, now drew his bow and sent an arrow into Diomedes' foot. The mighty Greek stumbled painfully to his chariot and drove off to the Greek encampment.

Odysseus was the next to be wounded. A spear tore through his flank, and so serious was the gash that the Trojans would have finished him off promptly had not Menelaus and Ajax come to his aid. As Ajax held up his towering shield for protection, Menelaus led Odysseus to his chariot, and to safety. Like a stubborn donkey tormented by boys, Ajax held his ground for a time; then he too fell back, and the rout was complete.

The retreating Greeks were forced to take refuge behind the wall they had built around their camp and ships, and here an even more furious battle took place. A blizzard of stones hissed over the battlefield in both directions as the Trojans tried to strike down the wall's defenders and the Greeks pelted the bronze-shielded attackers.

It was Hector who finally crashed through the Greek fortifications. He lifted a great rock – which two men living today could scarcely have budged – and heaved it at the gate. Its impact snapped the hinges, and the rock dropped within. Hector followed. Like a great boulder thundering down a hill through clumps of trees, he bounded and smashed through the Greeks until he reached their ships.

Hera's Scheme

Hera looked down from Olympus and saw the Greeks, her favourites, in flight. And on Mount Ida's peak she saw Zeus, happily contemplating the battlefield.

"How can I distract him from his plans?" she pondered. "I shall steal Aphrodite's girdle, for that is the secret of her charms. Then I will present myself to Zeus. When he sees me I will seem so irresistible that he will take me in his arms. The minute he does, I'll put him to sleep."

And that is exactly what happened. Immediately, the tide of battle turned. Hector, in his headlong rush to the ships, had just sent a spear into Ajax's breast-armour. But now the huge Greek, uninjured, hurled a boulder at Hector, which caught him at the base of the neck. Like a lightning-struck oak, Hector crashed to the ground and night fell on his eyes.

Now the Greeks took heart and hurled a volley of javelins, as Hector's lieutenants hastened to bear their great leader to safety. Ajax, amazingly fast despite his size, led his men forward, and the Trojans began to give way. As spear after spear tore into Trojan flesh, the Greeks took the offensive again.

Hector was brought to a river, and here his men tried to revive him by pouring water over him. He came to, sat up, and vomited blood, but again the blackness covered his eyes. Without their leader, the Trojans were in peril.

On Mount Ida, meanwhile, Zeus was awakening from his slumber. Suddenly, he sprang to his feet and stared at the battlefield. The Trojans were in flight! "Hera!" he bellowed. "Have you forgotten how I strung you from heaven with anvils at your heels?" Then he turned to the battlefield to exert his will. At once, Hector regained consciousness.

The Trojan leader stood up, power flowed back into his limbs, and he quickly set about regrouping his forces. When the Greeks saw this, they cried, "Hector has come back to life! This is the work of Zeus!" It was too much for them. Like a herd of cows stampeded by wild beasts, they turned and fled to their ships.

Ajax at the Ships

The Greeks scrambled up to the sterns of their warships. Here they snatched up the long bronze-tipped poles used in sea-fights and turned to face the surging Trojans. They jabbed and slashed at their attackers, while from deck to deck, like a skilled rider on horseback, Ajax ran to rally the Greeks.

"Have no fear", he roared, "but of dishonour! If you yield, you lose both life and honour!" In his hands was a great pike, thirty-three feet in length, which he swept back and forth, cutting huge swaths from the massed attackers.

But now Hector, like a wave whipped by a raging wind, was

flung against the ships by Zeus. Undaunted by Ajax's resounding shouts, he made for the very ship that the Greek was defending. He clasped its stern, and yelled, "Bring fire! Zeus gives us the victory!"

Ajax was under relentless attack. The arrows clanged against his helmet, his breath came in gasps, the sweat streamed over his aching hands, but still he swung his massive pike. Then Hector ended that. With one swipe of his sword he sheared the pole's bronze point clean off. At this, even Ajax shuddered and drew back. The Trojans threw torches into the ship and immediately it was ablaze.

It was a great triumph for the Trojans – but their last, for Zeus's obligations to Achilles and Thetis had now been fulfilled.

Patroclus

Patroclus, Achilles' closest friend, had been growing anxious about the Trojan onrush. "Agamemnon, Diomedes, Odysseus – three of our bravest warriors – are wounded," he moaned. "And the Greeks have been pushed back to the ships, while we have been sulking in our tents. If you will not fight, Achilles, lend me your armour and chariot, and I will lead our men into the battle. When the Trojans see me coming, they will think it is you and they will fall back."

But it was only when he saw the flames from the burning ships that Achilles became alarmed. "Go, Patroclus!" he cried. "They have set fire to the ships; we must save our means of retreat! Take my armour, while I wake the men."

So Patroclus, clad in Achilles' magnificent bronze and riding in a chariot drawn by the two matchless horses of Achilles, led the troops to battle. At the sight of this fresh battalion, seemingly led by the greatest of Greeks, the Trojans wavered, then turned and fled.

Even Hector could not arrest their retreat, for the apparent arrival of Achilles on the battlefield was enough to kindle panic in Trojan hearts. Across the Greek wall they streamed in headlong flight, hotly pursued by Patroclus, who shouted his war-cry as he hurled spears into their midst.

It was Hector that Patroclus sought. But only when the Trojans had been driven all the way to the gates of Troy did the two come face to face. Then Hector turned and instructed his charioteer to drive his horses straight at Patroclus. When the bold Greek saw them thundering down upon him, he leapt from his chariot, picked up a jagged stone, and threw it full force at Hector's driver. It shattered the fellow's forehead and he tumbled lifeless to the ground.

At once, several Trojans attempted to draw the man's body out of the way; but into their midst charged Patroclus, shouting fiercely. Three times he rushed in and three times he took a heavy toll. A fourth time he attacked, but with fatal results.

Apollo, hidden in a mist, came up behind Patroclus and, with one stroke of his hand, felled him. His helmet clattered to the ground, his shield fell from his shoulders, and his spear shattered. Patroclus was defenceless. Hector did not miss his chance, and drove his spear through Patroclus's belly.

Patroclus's soul took flight to the house of Hades, and from the corpse Hector stripped the armour of Achilles. He intended to strike off Patroclus's head, but the sudden advance of Ajax altered his plans. Clutching the prized armour, Hector stole from the scene.

Peace with Agamemnon

"Patroclus is dead!" cried the messenger, when he reached Achilles' tent. "Patroclus is dead!"

A black cloud of despair fell on Achilles. Great handfuls of dirt he took, and poured them on his head, and soiled his face. He sank to the ground, and tore at his hair. Such was his misery, as he groaned aloud his grief, that those around him feared that he would take a sword and cut his throat.

Thetis, hearing the outcries of her son, rose from the silver sea cave where she lived, and shortly appeared at his side. "Weep not, my son," she said. "Zeus has fulfilled your wish; through want of you, the Greeks have lost heavily!"

"Patroclus is dead," moaned Achilles. "What is life to me now? It is nothing – unless I kill Hector, who slew him!"

Thetis wept aloud. "Kill Hector," she said, "and you kill yourself! Soon after Hector's death, your own must come!"

"Then, if this be my fate," cried Achilles, "let me die!"

"If that be your intent," Thetis sighed, "I cannot hinder you. But your armour rests in Hector's hands. Tomorrow I will return with a new set of armour, forged by Hephaestus." With that, she left him.

The day, so disastrous to the Greeks, was ending. But before night fell the Trojans received an inkling of their doom, for suddenly, on the Greek wall, they saw a blazing figure, even brighter than the golden sunset. It was Achilles, whom Athena had filled with a godlike glow.

Then to the Trojan's ears came the sound of his voice, raised like a trumpet in a mighty battle cry. The Trojans were terrified. Their horses, scenting disaster, reared up and turned about. A second ringing shout Achilles gave, and a third. Though a bloody fight had been raging over the body of Patroclus, the Greeks now saw all opposition vanish, and they drew it away at last.

As Patroclus's torn body was borne back to the Greek camp, Achilles saw it and wept bitterly. All night the Greeks mourned for Patroclus, but Achilles vowed that his funeral would not be held until Hector had been slain.

On the morrow, the Greeks limped to an assembly, and there Achilles rose to speak. "Agamemnon," he said, "because of that girl, we have been enemies. But who has profited by our feud? Only Hector, and the Trojans! My anger with you is at an end. Now, if you will call us to battle, I will do my utmost."

The Greeks shouted their approval and Agamemnon rose to reply. "I, too, dispel my anger. Curse the day it began! Arm yourself, Achilles, and lead the army to battle."

And what armour Achilles donned! His eyes took fire as he looked upon the marvellous gear that his mother had brought him from Hephaestus's forge. Gnashing his teeth, he clasped the greaves around his legs, the cuirass about his breast, and the silver-hilted sword on his shoulder. Then he lifted up the thick shield, gleaming like the moon, and the golden-plumed helmet. Achilles tested the suppleness of his armour, and it seemed to lift him like wings. Finally, he took up his father's spear – strong, heavy and long.

Like snow-flakes before a driving storm, the Greeks swept onto the battlefield. The Trojans too poured into the plain, until it was filled with horses and men. A great battle was in the offing, but with Achilles again in the Greek ranks there could be no doubt of the issue.

The Fight with Hector

Achilles attacked the Trojans, and his spears went everywhere – into the breasts, the bowels, the brains of the Trojans. He hunted his victims like a fiend, striking them down until the earth was darkened with their blood. Like oxen trampling barley on the threshing-floor, the horses of Achilles trampled upon dead men and cast-off shields. On drove Achilles, spattering his invincible hands with gore.

High on the walls of Troy, old King Priam saw Achilles impelling the Trojans to retreat. With a cry of alarm he called to the watchmen below: "Hold open the gates until our men have entered, and then shut them fast." Soon, like trembling deer, the Trojans were crowding into the city.

Suddenly, Priam cried aloud. Hector, intent on battle with Achilles, had taken a stand before the gates. "Hector!" he cried. "My son! Do not meet this demon alone! He is stronger than you, and he will destroy you! Come inside the walls and live to be our protector!"

But Hector stood his ground. Like a mountain snake glaring at a man approaching his den, he waited, coiled for the attack. On came Achilles, his bronze armour shining like the sun, his terrible spear poised over the right shoulder. It was too much, even for Hector. He trembled and began to fall back.

But, like a hawk, Achilles was after him. It was a nightmare chase – though they exerted themselves to the breaking point, the distance between them did not change. Around the walls of Troy they ran, three times.

It was only with the assistance of Apollo that Hector had been able to keep ahead of his pursuer, however, and now Apollo deserted him. At the command of Zeus, Hermes took up the golden scales of destiny. In one balance he placed the life of Achilles, in the other that of Hector. Down came the beam, down to Hades – on the side of Hector!

Now Hector came to a halt, and turned to face Achilles. "I will fight now," he said. "If I win, I shall do no outrage to your body and I ask that you do the same."

"No bargains!" said Achilles. "You will pay for your slaughter to the full!" He cast his spear. Hector crouched, and it flew over him; then he too swung his spear up to his shoulder and hurled it. Into the centre of Achilles' shield it smashed – and was deflected away.

⌐th had thrown their only spears, but Achilles had his again, for Athena had retrieved it. Now Hector drew his sword and swept down on Achilles. He waited, scrutinizing his attacker, and then he flung his spear.

Achilles aimed at one small target. In that armour, he knew, there was but one opening, and the point of his spear found it. It tore into the flesh of Hector's neck.

Down came the mighty Trojan into the dust, and Achilles shouted in triumph. "Fool! When you were stripping Patroclus you thought yourself safe. Now, while we are holding his funeral rites, the dogs and vultures will maul you!"

"I beseech you", whispered Hector, "to take a ransom for my body. My father and mother will pay you abundantly."

"No ransom, be it twenty times your worth," snarled Achilles, "will keep the scavengers from your flesh."

"Think what you are saying," said dying Hector, "lest I bring upon you the wrath of the gods." And his soul left his body and flew down to the house of Hades, bewailing its fate.

"Die!" said Achilles. He pulled the bloody armour from the corpse. The other Greeks gathered round, and were at once struck by the beauty of Hector's body.

But now Achilles performed a hideous deed. Hector's mother, when she saw it, tore her hair and cried aloud, and Priam, moaning piteously, had to be prevented from rushing through the gates at Achilles. Andromache, when she saw this dismal thing, fell back gasping and the world went black before her eyes.

Achilles had slit the tendons of Hector's feet from heel to ankle, and bound them with leather straps to his chariot. Then he had driven across the plain, leaving Hector's head to drag in the dust.

Priam

On a great funeral pyre, the corpse of Patroclus was cremated. But the wrongs done to Hector's body endured. Day after day, Achilles dragged it around Patroclus's tomb. When the gods saw this, they were filled with anger; even Zeus was wrathful. Thus, they inspired King Priam to an act of great courage.

Priam had a cart loaded with the finest treasures of Troy, and set out with it for the Greek camp. Hermes aided him, causing the Greek sentries to drowse, and throwing open the gates. Then Priam entered the tent of Achilles.

Achilles was struck with amazement. The father of Hector knelt before him, clasped his knees, and kissed his hands. "Think, Achilles," said Priam, "of your own father. He is my age, but he still has this hope – that his son will some day return from battle.

I have no such hope. Accept the ransom I have brought, and give me the body of my son. See, Achilles, what I do! I kiss the hands of my son's slayer!"

Achilles was filled with admiration for Priam's courage. Taking the old man's arm, he raised him up gently. Then he fulfilled his request. As the ransom was taken from Priam's wagon, Achilles directed his servants to wash and anoint the body of Hector. Despite the treatment it had received, the flesh was still unmarred, for Apollo had protected it.

So Priam returned with the body of his son. In the light of dawn, the people of Troy saw his approach and they thronged to meet him outside the gate. Wailing a dirge, the procession wound through the streets of Troy. For nine days the mourners, assured of safety by Achilles, went outside the city gates to gather great quantities of wood for the funeral pyre. On the tenth it was set ablaze, and the body of Hector was consumed.

The Death of Achilles

The battle of Troy continued. From the north came Amazons to reinforce the hard-pressed Trojans. But, when Achilles slew their queen, their fighting spirit evaporated. Then Ethiopians arrived from the south. Achilles triumphed over their leader also, and the enemy turned in retreat. As Achilles led the exultant Greeks onwards, he boasted that even the gods of Olympus were powerless against his onrushes.

It was just at this moment that the gods struck him down. Apollo appeared to Paris, who was shooting random arrows into the attacking Greeks. "Why waste your shafts on ordinary warriors?" he said. "Direct your aim at Achilles, and gain vengeance for the death of Hector!" Paris shot, and Apollo guided the arrow into Achilles' heel.

Achilles crumbled to the ground, for the wound was fatal. Despite his mother's precautions, Achilles had not been made immortal. Where the water of the River Styx had touched him, he was indeed invulnerable. But there was one place against which the waters had not washed, for Thetis had held the infant by the heel.

When the Trojans and their allies saw the fall of Achilles, they swept back into battle, intent on making off with the corpse. But they were not to succeed. Odysseus, like a lioness defending her cubs against marauding hunters, fended off their attacks, while Ajax strode away with Achilles' body upon his shoulder.

So yet another funeral pyre was erected, and on its summit were placed the remains of the greatest of heroes. The torch was applied and the fire roared through the logs. And, when the flames had died, only a handful of ashes remained.

15
THE
WANDERINGS
OF ODYSSEUS

It is tempting to regard the shrewd battler Odysseus as a legendary figure. And it is quite possible that a certain king of Ithaca did encounter difficulties in returning home after fighting at Troy. One man, who believes that Odysseus's voyage happened much as described, has spent many years searching the shores of the Mediterranean for clues. In Sicily he has discovered caves very similar to those of the Cyclopes. He has investigated the Straits of Messina and has determined the whereabouts of Scylla and Charybdis. And after a lengthy search he has found, on the southern coast of Corsica, a harbour like that of the Lestrygons – long and narrow, and flanked by high cliffs.

However, it seems clear that the story of Odysseus also includes

British Museum

138

traces of myth. Some have interpreted the stringing of the Great Bow as a ritual for the selection of a new king. Ordinarily the previous king would be shot down by the one who could string the bow but (according to this theory) Odysseus rebels, and by stringing the bow himself renews his own kingship.

The boar-wound on Odysseus's thigh has also been taken as a sign that he has avoided being sacrificed. Adonis was gored to death by a boar, and it was while Seth was hunting boar that he slew Osiris. Circe – another custodian of the Land of Death – humbles men by turning them into swine, but Odysseus avoids this fate also. One intriguing detail concerns Monte Circeo on the coast of Italy, where Circe's hut has been located. In a cave on this hill has been found the evidence of a Neanderthal ritual like that described on page 5. In the earlier ritual, the skull of a bear was placed on its own bones, but at Monte Circeo the skull and bones were those of a man.

(The vase painting at the left shows Odysseus escaping from the cave of Polyphemus.)

The Armour of Achilles

Achilles was dead. Who now deserved to wear his armour? Ajax, who had carried Achilles' body out of the Trojans' grasp? Odysseus, who had held them at bay? Ajax, the giant? Or Odysseus, the brilliant schemer? When a vote had been taken to settle the issue, the armour of Achilles was awarded to Odysseus.

When Ajax learned of the decision, he was so overcome with disappointment that he went mad with rage. Seeing a flock of sheep, he took them to be Greek soldiers and slaughtered scores of them. One, which he imagined to be Odysseus, he tied to a pillar and whipped.

When his fury had been exhausted and he had come to his senses, Ajax looked about in astonishment at the havoc he had wrought. His disgrace was complete; nothing was left but suicide. He knelt down, buried his sword-hilt in the earth, and flung himself upon the blade.

Few of the Greek heroes had survived ten years of war, but, of those who had, the greatest was Odysseus. Now he was to prove his right to that title.

The Wooden Horse

There came a day of great rejoicing for the people of Troy. Neither at sea nor on land were any Greek warships to be seen, and nothing remained of the Greek camp but ashes. The Greeks had gone!

And before the walls of Troy stood a horse, high as a hill, constructed of wooden planks.

When the Trojans saw it, a bitter dispute broke out among them. "Bring it within the walls!" urged one.

"Push it into the sea!" cried another.

"Burn it!" demanded a third.

"No, no!" another shouted. "It is sacred to Athena." And indeed, carved on the flank of the horse were these words: "For their safe return, the Greeks dedicate this offering to Athena."

Then the priest, Laocoon, spoke: "Are you mad, citizens? How could anyone trust Greeks, even when they bring gifts? Know you not the cunning Odysseus? This wood conceals Greeks!" He hurled his spear; it quivered in the horse's side, and the cavern within echoed hollowly.

Sinon

Just then a Greek soldier, in shackles, was brought forward to King Priam. Through the outcry aroused by his appearance, the man, whose name was Sinon, made himself heard. "Will no land receive me? The Greeks have cast me out, and now the Trojans demand my blood!"

The tumult subsided and the crowd pressed forward to hear Sinon's tale. "Yes, they have gone," he said. "And before they departed, I was to have been sacrificed! An oracle told them that a Greek life was needed to give them a safe journey home. See the ritual headband still round my temples! But I escaped them and hid all night in the swamp. I dread to think what they will do to my father and my son."

Moved by the story, Priam at once ordered Sinon's shackles to be removed. Asked about the wooden horse, the Greek replied that this had been built as an offering to the goddess Athena. "But why was it made of such enormous size?" asked Priam.

"It is no sin", Sinon replied, "to reveal the secrets of the Greeks. They hoped that you might not drag it within the walls. If you did, you would have the power to invade Greece. But what they especially hoped was that you would damage it, for then Athena's wrath would be upon you!"

At this moment, a startling event occurred. Two monstrous snakes, their blood-red coils arching over the blue waves and lashing the surface to foam, hissed over the water towards Laocoon. Within moments, they had wrapped themselves about his two sons and crushed out their lives. Then they caught Laocoon in their strangling grip – twice they coiled about his waist, twice about his neck, and still their red bodies towered above him. Like a bull struck at the altar, Laocoon cried out his last. The snakes slithered into the temple of Athena and vanished.

The people of Troy hesitated no longer. Laocoon had profaned the offering to Athena and had been punished. "Bring the horse to Athena's temple!" they cried. So the walls which for ten years had turned back the Greeks were breached to allow entry for the hollow horse.

In their first day of peace, the Trojans feasted and celebrated. Into the night the revelry continued, till sleep overcame them. They did not see Sinon making his way to the shore, there to light a beacon fire. They did not see the answering light on the bow of Agamemnon's ship, concealed with the other ships behind a wooded island. But, to the eager eyes of Greeks sailing again for the Trojan shore, the appearance of a third, and brighter, light could mean only one thing. The Greek warriors hidden in the horse's belly had emerged and had plunged the city into flames.

The Sack of Troy

The wooden horse had been the scheme of Odysseus. He had also planned Sinon's trick. And now it was Odysseus who led the Greeks out of the horse and through the streets of Troy.

The Trojans were helpless. When they awoke, they could hear only shouting and shrieking, and they could see red flickers of fire slashing the blackness. When they entered the streets, the Greek war bands which now overran the city cut them down. By now, the Greek ships had disgorged their men, and the soldiers had swept across the plain and through the breached wall. This was not war – it was slaughter.

A river of warriors rushed upon the royal palace and burst through the doors. Priam donned armour he had not used for years and waited with Queen Hecuba and their daughters at the family altar. When the first soldier strode towards them, the old king cast his spear; it clanged feebly against the aggressor's shield. Then the Greek struck him down and cast his body unburied upon Athena's altar.

Elsewhere, Menelaus was prowling the streets with but one purpose in mind – to find Helen and slay her. Paris was dead, but bitterness and jealousy still possessed Menelaus's soul. When he found her, he raised his sword to kill her, but Helen fell to her knees before him. Recalling all the suffering she had caused, Menelaus brought his sword up for the fatal stroke – and it fell from his hand. Her beauty had conquered him.

The work of destruction went on through the night and into the morning, until Troy had been reduced to ashes. The Trojan women were herded together and assigned to Greek masters, while the males – all who had not escaped – were slain. Hector's prayers for his son were to go unanswered, for the child was thrown from the walls to the rocks below.

The Greeks had been too brutal, however, and the anger of the gods was aroused. When Cassandra, a priestess of Athena, took refuge in her temple and clung to an image of the goddess, a Greek soldier had dragged her from it. Athena, enraged by this sacrilege, vowed to make the return voyage of the Greeks disastrous. She called upon Poseidon to help her.

Thus, Menelaus was to be driven from his course by storms, and to spend many years finding his way to Sparta, and Agamemnon was to return home sooner only to meet the grimmest of fates. But the man who would suffer the longest was Odysseus.

The Lotus Eaters

Soon after Odysseus left ravaged Troy, his ships were caught in the grip of strong currents and relentless winds. The crews desperately struggled to round the southernmost cape of Greece and sail northwards to their home, the island of Ithaca, but Poseidon was stronger. For nine days they were swept across the sea-god's realm; on the tenth they made land. The exhausted crews went ashore for a midday meal and Odysseus sent some of his men inland to explore the region. When they failed to return, Odysseus set off after them. He found them in a blissful stupor, with no intention of rejoining their companions. They had come among the lotus-eaters, who eat only the honeyed fruit of the lotus which takes away all thoughts save of the pleasure of eating it.

When Odysseus attempted to draw them away, they struggled and pleaded to be left alone, to eat of the lotus forever. By brute force, however, Odysseus brought them to the ship and chained them under the benches. Then he weighed anchor at once, to prevent any others from falling victim to the drug.

Polyphemus

When next the sailors came ashore, Odysseus took with him twelve of his crew to find out what creatures inhabited the land. They found a cave, obviously the home of a shepherd, and entered to await the owner's return. Soon they heard the bleating of sheep; then they saw their bobbing forms crowd into the cave, and finally the shepherd himself. He was a Cyclops.

The deafening clatter of wood being thrown inside the cave's mouth sent the men scuttling deeper into the cave. From there they watched the Cyclops, whose name was Polyphemus, close the doorway. So enormous was the stone he used, that twenty teams of oxen could not have budged it. Then, after milking his ewes, Polyphemus lit a fire and, by its light, spied his visitors.

"Ha! What are you?" he boomed.

Polyphemus listened to Odysseus's reply. Then, snatching up two men as if they were puppets, he dashed out their brains on the ground, and devoured them – flesh, bones, and marrow. Satiated, the Cyclops stretched out and fell asleep. Odysseus would have crept up to the creature and plunged his sword into its heart, but then the stone could not have been moved aside.

Morning came, and the Cyclops swallowed another two men for his breakfast. Then, whistling happily, he hefted the great boulder aside and drove his flocks out to pasture – making sure to replace the huge stone when he departed.

Odysseus groped desperately for some plan of action. At last he had one. A green log, big as a mast, lay in the cave. He directed his men to sharpen it to a point; then, before Polyphemus came thudding into the cave, they hid it in the dirt.

That evening the Cyclops gobbled down two more terrified Greeks. Then Odysseus began to execute his plan.

"Won't you have some wine, Cyclops, to finish off that meal properly?" he said. "I brought you this gift in hope that you would treat me kindly." His host picked up the bowl, and swallowed its contents at a gulp.

"More!" he demanded. "Then tell me your name, and I will grant you a favour." Three more bowlfuls went down that cavernous gullet, and the Cyclops seemed satisfied.

"Cyclops," said Odysseus, "my name is Nobody."

"Nobody," grunted Polyphemus, "I will eat you last. That is the favour I will grant you." With that, he toppled forward heavy with drink.

Now Odysseus and his men set to work. They heated the point of the log in a fire until it glowed white-hot. Then they raised it over their shoulders, and rammed the point into the Cyclops's eye. Like a man boring a hole in a ship's timber, Odysseus leaned on the end of the log and twisted it. With a horrible shriek, Polyphemus plucked out the log and flung it down.

His neighbours, hearing the terrible outcry, came running; but, when they asked what the matter was, he roared, "Nobody has blinded me!"

"Well," they said, "if nobody has blinded you, you are sick. Pray to the gods, but stop that racket!"

Now Odysseus carried out the rest of his plan. Making as little noise as possible, he lashed together three thick-woolled rams, and under the middle one tied one of his men. Six times he did this – for only six of his companions remained. Odysseus himself selected one particularly fleecy ram and curled himself under its shaggy belly, clutching the wool firmly. Then with gnawing anxiety they awaited the dawn, when Polyphemus would release the sheep again.

Dawn arrived, and the blinded Cyclops pushed back the stone once more and the flock began to move through the doorway. Polyphemus sat beside the opening, feeling the backs of the animals as they passed by. But he failed to notice any of the men lashed beneath.

Finally, the ram under which Odysseus crouched began to trot through the doorway. "What is this?" demanded Polyphemus, as he passed his hand along the animal's back. "You have never lagged behind the others. Do you take pity on your poor master, blinded by Nobody? If only you could tell me where he is hiding! Then I would soak the floor with his brains!"

He let the ram go, and immediately Odysseus relinquished his grip and hurried about untying his companions. Soon the men were rowing away from shore.

But Odysseus could not resist bidding Polyphemus farewell. "Cyclops!" he shouted. "Now you have been paid for your hospitality!"

The words were not wasted on Polyphemus. Enraged, he ripped off the top of a hill and sent it whistling into the sea just ahead of the ship's bows. The wave raised by it shoved the vessel back almost to the beach. Grasping a long pole, Odysseus thrust the ship away from the land and urged his men to row for their lives. When they had gone twice as far as before, a huge boulder plunged into the sea. But this one fell just astern, and the swell carried the ship beyond the range of any further farewell gifts.

Aeolia

Next they came to the floating island of Aeolia, where they received a more gracious welcome. For a month the king entertained them with a constant stream of banquets and luxuries. When the time came for departure, Odysseus received a most welcome gift. The king, whom Zeus had appointed Warden of the Winds, handed him a large ox-hide bag.

"If you keep the neck of the bag tightly closed with this silver wire," he explained, "all will be well. For all the winds are imprisoned within this bag, except for a gentle westerly breeze which will carry you home."

Full of gratitude, Odysseus set sail. For nine days his ships were wafted across the Mediterranean; on the tenth, Ithaca came in view. Then, when they were actually close enough to see the people at their fires, Odysseus fell asleep.

"What is in that bag?" asked the crew members among themselves. "Look at us – empty-handed after our long voyage, while he is in all likelihood concealing plunder. Let us see what silver and gold he is hiding." They undid the silver wire, and the turbulent winds sprang forth. Instantly, the ships were swept out to sea.

Odysseus, when he awoke to see his homeland receding from view, almost threw himself overboard. But he restrained himself, and after several days the floating island of Aeolia again came into view. Odysseus went ashore, but met a different reception. To his sorrowful explanation and appeal for new aid, the king replied,

"Away with you, worst of sinners! You have misused my gift. Your presence here is an insult to the gods!"

The Lestrygons

After seven days' journeying they came to yet another unfamiliar land. They dropped anchor in a fine harbour enclosed by steep cliffs – all but Odysseus and his crew, who secured their own ship just outside the cove. Three men sent inland came upon a girl of sturdy proportions, the daughter of the chief of these people, called the Lestrygons. She directed them to her home, where her mother, an enormous creature, and her father, who was larger still, awaited them. When the girl's father unceremoniously devoured one of the sailors, the others ran for their lives.

The chief's bellows brought the other Lestrygons running from every direction. From the cliffs surrounding the harbour the gigantic creatures hurled down showers of rocks on the unfortunate men, then speared them like fish and carried them off to make wretched meals.

Odysseus, as soon as he caught a glimpse of this nightmare, hacked through the anchor rope with his sword, and his men rowed like madmen. But for the ships in the harbour there was no escape.

Circe

Worn by grief and fatigue, the survivors came ashore next at the wooded island of Aeaea. To the dismay of his followers, Odysseus again proposed that an exploring party be sent out. Lots were cast, and, while Odysseus stayed behind with half of the crew, the other twenty-two sallied forth.

In a clearing in the forest, the searchers came upon a stone house, around which lurked lions and wolves. Far from intending harm, the animals stood on their hind legs, with tails wagging, to lick the men's hands. Unnerved by this experience, the sailors proceeded to the house, from which came the sound of a female voice raised in song. They shouted, the music ceased, and through the doorway walked a beautiful woman, bearing a wand in her hand. This was Circe, the enchantress.

She invited the men to enter and all of them did so except for their leader, who suspected a trap. The hungry men were given bowls filled with a mixture of cheese, meal, honey, wine – and a drug. When they had eaten, Circe touched them with her wand.

Suddenly, bristles sprouted from their bodies, cleft hooves formed on their feet, and from their flattened noses came wheezing grunts. They had been turned into pigs! Their minds were still those of men, however, and, as they were herded into muddy pigsties, they wept.

Horror-stricken at the sight of his comrades' transformation, the leader of the group ran back to the ship to relate his unhappy tale. Odysseus, though he had no definite plans, armed himself and set off into the forest. On his way he met with good fortune, for Hermes appeared and gave him invaluable advice.

"Take this herb," said the god, offering Odysseus a milk-white flower with a black root. "When Circe gives you food, you must smell this as an antidote to her drugs. When she strikes you with her wand, draw your sword and threaten her with her life. She will be in your power."

Hermes vanished into the forest, and Odysseus was soon facing the beautiful enchantress. Everything happened as the god had foretold. When Odysseus sprang at Circe with drawn sword, she fell sobbing at his feet.

When he demanded the release of his men, Circe opened the pigsty, and drove out the swine. On each of them she rubbed another of her drugs. One by one, the pigs lost their bristles and took on the form of men – but younger than before, taller, and more handsome.

As the men, uncontrollably happy, gathered about Odysseus, Circe said, "Go to the shore, Odysseus. Draw your ship onto the land, and return with the rest of your men." Odysseus did not hesitate to do so. Indeed, so charming had their hostess become that they stayed for an entire year.

Tiresias

When Odysseus began to talk of returning to Ithaca, Circe said: "Before you depart, you must consult the spirit of Tiresias, the blind prophet of Thebes. He will foretell what awaits you on your journey and at its end. Spread your sails now, and let the North Wind carry you to the Grove of Persephone, to a place where two rivers pour their waters into the Underworld. There you will dig a trench and slit the throats of a ram and a ewe, letting their blood fill the trench. The spirits of the dead will cluster about it, for they love to drink fresh blood. But hold them back with your sword until Tiresias has spoken."

Great was the depression of his men when Odysseus told them that they would next go to the land of death. But they obeyed, and soon full sails were propelling them to the foggy regions of the two rivers. There Odysseus followed Circe's instructions.

The ghosts rose up to the trench of blood in a wailing host. Even great Odysseus went pale with dread when he looked upon the souls of old men mingling with those of young maidens, and of warriors with open wounds. But with out-thrust sword he kept them at bay, until at length Tiresias appeared. Odysseus then turned his sword aside, and the prophet stooped to drink the dark blood.

"Hardships await you," said Tiresias. "Poseidon still intends harm to you, but another, Hyperion the Sun-Titan, you must especially avoid offending. You will come to the island on which his cattle graze. Let them not be touched, or your ship and all its crew are doomed!"

Tiresias drank again of the blood, and continued: "In Ithaca, too, there will be troubles. A riotous mob of suitors is plaguing your house. You must kill them all. Even then you will not find rest, for you will set forth again on your travels. And from the sea your death will come – but the gentlest of deaths it will be."

Tiresias descended into the House of Hades. Odysseus stayed at the trench, however, for he was eager to speak to the souls of some that he had recognized. Among them was Agamemnon. The living Greek allowed the dead one to drink; then, overcome with pity, Odysseus cried out, "Agamemnon, king of men! What fate brought you to this lamentable end?"

"Odysseus," answered the fallen commander-in-chief, "you have beheld the slaughter of men in bloody battle, but never have you seen so horrible a sight as my death-throes. In my own palace was I struck down, at the hands of my wretched wife, and her lover! Even as I lay dying, the vile creature was not even so kind as to shut my staring eyes. Clytemnestra has brought shame on all womankind forever!"

As they talked sadly, the soul of great Achilles rose into view. "Achilles, most blessed of men!" cried Odysseus. "On earth you were honoured like the gods; here, among the dead, you are a prince. Death can be no misery for you."

"Offer no praise of death, Odysseus," answered Achilles mournfully. "If I could live on the ground again, even as the slave of a landless farmer, I would prefer that to kingship over dead men." Then he vanished.

Hordes of spirits now swarmed around Odysseus, hoping to question this visitor from the earth. Only Ajax, still sulking over the defeat he had suffered over the armour of Achilles, kept his distance. Odysseus tried to soothe the great warrior's spirit by telling of the continuing sorrow of all Greeks for his death, but Ajax said nothing, and moved off, to be lost from view.

Now throngs without number, moaning clamorously, beset Odysseus, until panic laid hold of him and he retreated to the ship.

The Sirens

Returning to Aeaea, Odysseus and his crew devoted one last day to feasting at Circe's expense. The enchantress added to Tiresias's counsel, advising Odysseus how the next perils should be met. At dawn the journey began.

As they approached the first of these dangers, Odysseus instructed his men: "Soon we will pass the island of the Sirens. No man has heard their voices and returned to tell of it. Today I shall listen to their song, and survive. But you must tie me securely to the mast; otherwise, I would undoubtedly leap from the ship and swim to the island – and certain death. To preserve you from the fate they have in store for us, I will stop your ears with bees-wax."

Even as these arrangements were being made, a strange calm descended on the sea. And, as they attacked the still waters with their oars, the island appeared out of the haze. Then the sailors saw, but luckily did not hear, the Sirens themselves.

The ship drew closer, and the men could see something else. The island was littered with corpses, from the bones of which skin still drooped.

Meanwhile, Odysseus was suffering from the torments of the Sirens' song – a melody of indescribable loveliness. As the rowers swiftly bore him away from it, he ordered his men to set him free. But they saw only his working mouth, his fierce frowns, his jerking head, for their ears were stopped. Immune to the Sirens' power, they only tightened the ropes about him and rowed on. After several miles they removed the bees-wax and released their captain.

Scylla and Charybdis

As soon as this danger had passed, another presented itself. Smoke spewed out of the sea ahead, and the surf roared so deafeningly that the sailors let their oars fall from their grip. A narrow strait lay ahead; on the one side was a violent whirlpool, and on the other a huge rock that ascended into the clouds.

"Row with all speed," shouted Odysseus encouragingly. "And, steersman, keep us hard by those cliffs and away from this whirlpool."

Circe had warned Odysseus of the monster Charybdis, who three times a day swallowed the sea water with a terrifying rumble, and three times spouted it forth like a boiling cauldron. But the other peril of the strait Odysseus could by no means describe to his men. Half-way up the sheer rock, in a cave that reached down to Tartarus, sat Scylla, whose yelps were like those of a new-born dog. From the cave stretched Scylla's six long necks, each tipped with a ghastly head containing three rows of murderous teeth. Six of Odysseus's men, Circe had warned, would be victims of those teeth.

Thrashing oars now propelled the ship past Charybdis, whose spray fell all around. Gripping two spears, Odysseus scanned the rock above for a glimpse of Scylla, but none was to be found. Then, as he turned about to glance over his crew, he saw the arms and legs of six sailors already jerked up into the air by the monster, like small fish whipped from the sea by an angler's rod. They cried out piteously, but it was too late to save them.

The strait had taken its toll, and now the ship was through. So the men sailed on – to the worst peril of all.

The Island of the Sun

In the evening the ship drew near an island from which rose the sound of lowing cattle. This, Odysseus knew, was the island of Hyperion. Here the men landed for the night, but not before Odysseus had exacted from them a solemn oath that none of the sacred cattle of Hyperion would be touched.

In the night a wild gale descended on the island. For a month the winds kept the ship penned in, while provisions dwindled and at last gave out. Half-starved, the men prowled the island in search of wild game and fish.

One day Odysseus went off alone to pray to the gods. But in his weakness he fell asleep, and, when he awoke and rushed back to the ship, the worst of his fears had been realized. The sweet odour of roasting beef filled the air. Odysseus rebuked the men violently, but more frightening to them even than their captain's words were the slain cattle themselves. Their flesh, even on the spits, bellowed aloud, and their hides crawled.

The gale dropped, and the men embarked. But a black cloud hovered overhead and soon Zeus, to whom Hyperion had appealed, took vengeance. With one bolt he blasted the ship.

The crew, scattered on the waves, bobbed like gulls until the sea could support them no longer. None but Odysseus survived. Clinging to the mast, he rode out the worst that the sea offered, and came at last to the island home of Calypso.

Calypso

Seven years was Odysseus the prisoner of beautiful Calypso. In her cavern by the sea, she loved him and cared for him tenderly, wishing to make him immortal like herself. But she could not win his love. Day after day, with aching heart, Odysseus sat on the shore staring across the sea in the direction of his distant home.

His wife Penelope, as he knew from Tiresias's words, was being troubled continually by a band of scoundrels who demanded that she select one of them as her husband. For a while, Penelope had used a trick to postpone her decision. Setting up a great web on her loom, she had promised to declare her choice as soon as she had finished her weaving. For years she had fooled them by un-ravelling her work by night, but eventually her trick was dis-covered. Now her suitors were more restless than ever.

Even Athena, whose anger against the Greeks had sent Odys-seus on his wanderings, took pity on him. Poseidon was as ill-disposed as ever, but, when he left Olympus for a brief journey, Athena begged Zeus to permit Odysseus to return homeward safely. He agreed, and Calypso was informed of the gods' decision.

To Odysseus's surprise, he received one day from his captor an axe, and other tools. "Go," wept lovely Calypso. "Since you will never be mine, build a ship and leave me. I myself will provide you with sails and food for your journey."

Overjoyed, Odysseus set to work, and in four days he had constructed a sturdy vessel. On the fifth he bade Calypso farewell, and she saw him drift to the horizon, and beyond.

Phaeacia

Still were Odysseus's mishaps to continue. As he approached the land of the Phaeacians, he was spied by Poseidon, and at once the sea-god sent a massive wave that dashed Odysseus from his boat. Another giant wave, and the vessel was in splinters.

Odysseus swam the heavy seas, doggedly making his way towards the shore, but as he came closer he found that the coast was ringed with jagged rocks. Another mountainous wave caught him, and he was flung onwards. Frantically, Odysseus clutched at an off-shore boulder before the wave could sweep him onto the rocks. Then the backwash ripped him from his hold with a violence that peeled strips of skin from his hands and left them sticking to the boulder.

Now Odysseus fought his way beyond the breakers and swam parallel to the shore, scanning the shore for a landing-place. At length he found an accessible river-mouth. Wearily, he swam up-stream and stumbled ashore to fall heavily asleep.

Nausicaa

The King of Phaeacia had a young daughter named Nausicaa, beautiful as a goddess. In the morning, she and her maids came to the river to wash their linen in its bubbling pools. Competing with each other to be finished first, they trod their clothes until they were spotless and spread them out to dry. As they waited for the sun to perform its task, they tossed a ball back and forth. When white-armed Nausicaa threw it to one of her maids, she missed, and it fell into the river. Their excited screams woke Odysseus.

Like a mountain lion he strode from the bushes under which he had been sleeping. At the sight of his salt-caked body, from which the waves had torn his clothing, the girls scampered away – all but Nausicaa. Odysseus halted, uncertain how to explain his case.

"I kneel before you, princess," he said, "or are you a goddess?

For never have I beheld your equal in loveliness. Troubles have beset me. Twenty days have I struggled on the wine-dark sea, and now I ask only that you provide me with some humble garment and lead me to your town."

"Your words show you to be neither villain nor fool," Nausicaa replied. "I will fulfil your wishes." And she called to her maids to bring Odysseus suitable clothing. When he had bathed himself in the river and donned fresh garments, he was brought to the Phaeacian palace.

The king entertained their guest well, with feasting, dancing, minstrelcy, and games. In return, Odysseus told the story of his adventures with such vividness that an awed silence ensued. Then the king, eager to aid the unfortunate man, decreed that the next day his sailors would convey Odysseus to Ithaca.

And so, within a few hours, the wanderer had come home.

Telemachus

After twenty years – ten years at Troy and ten years of wanderings – Odysseus had at last returned to Ithaca, and to his greatest test – for Tiresias had said that all the suitors were to be slain. But what support could Odysseus hope to find against that hostile mob?

Now Athena, in order that Odysseus might proceed unobserved, disguised him as a beggar. At a touch, the goddess withered the flesh of his muscular limbs, bereft his head of its locks, and dimmed the light of his eyes. In this guise, the King of Ithaca shambled up the hills to the hut of his faithful old swineherd.

To the same destination, Athena had directed another of the suitors' foes – Odysseus's son, Telemachus. He was returning to Ithaca after a trip through Greece in search of his father. For the opposition he had shown them, the suitors had plotted to ambush the young prince. Following the instructions of Athena, however, he had evaded them.

In the hut, meanwhile, the swine-herd, not recognizing his disguised master, had provided him with a meal. He was describing angrily the gluttonous appetites of the suitors, who slaughtered the choicest of Odysseus's animals day and night, when Telemachus appeared at the threshold.

Odysseus quickly rose to offer him his seat, but his son checked him gently. Then, when the swine-herd left the hut, Athena transformed Odysseus to his former self. Telemachus averted his eyes in astonishment, saying, "Surely you are a god. Be gracious, that I may sacrifice to you!"

"You see no god," replied Odysseus. "I am your father."

He kissed his son. Slowly, the truth dawned on Telemachus. Then, throwing himself on his father's neck, he cried tears of relief.

Antinous

Soon they set to work to determine a course of action. The walls of the hall occupied by the suitors were hung with spears and shields. These, it was decided, were to be gathered up and stored in the strong-room – all but a few, to be readily available for their use. Odysseus would resume his beggar's guise and thus spy on his enemies.

Now Telemachus made his way to the palace. He was followed shortly by his father, again in his ragged garb, and accompanied by the old swine-herd.

As Odysseus shuffled along, he saw a dog, infested with vermin, lying abandoned on a dung-heap. The hound lifted its head, pricked up its ears, and wagged its tail feebly. And, having seen its master once again, the dog died.

Once again Odysseus stepped into the great hall of his palace. Here the noisy mob of suitors was lounging, after banqueting on freshly slaughtered meats. To these unwelcome rogues, one after the other, Odysseus stretched out his hand, begging for scraps of food.

"Swine-herd!" barked one of the suitors, called Antinous. "Why did you bring along this fellow? Aren't we plagued with enough of these pests?"

Odysseus took no heed of the oaf for the moment, but when he came to him in his rounds he spoke out: "Your contribution, sir. You are certainly not the least of these men, but the best, for you are like a prince. Therefore I have reason to expect better alms from you, and I will sing your praises throughout the world."

"What has brought this villain here?" Antinous shouted. "Get away from here, you rascal!"

"Why, hasn't this man the intelligence to match his noble looks!" Odysseus exclaimed. "You sit at another man's table, and cannot give a morsel of bread to a beggar!"

Enraged, Antinous picked up a footstool and hurled it viciously at Odysseus, striking him on the back. But Odysseus stood firm as a rock, and only shook his head silently before moving away to the threshold. Here a further indignity awaited him.

Irus

Another beggar approached. Seeing in Odysseus a potential rival, he shouted out: "Be off with you, old man, or I'll drag you away!"

When Odysseus gave a firm reply, the beggar, whose name was Irus, cried out: "Now these gentlemen will see a fight! Or do you dare to face a younger man?"

The suitors, when they heard these words, jumped merrily from their tables and clustered around the pair. But, when they saw Odysseus bare his broad shoulders and sinewy arms, they exchanged startled glances. Irus trembled with fear and had to be dragged before his opponent.

After considering for a moment whether to deal the braggart a deadly blow, or merely to prostrate him with a light thrust, Odysseus struck Irus on the jaw, so that he fell whimpering to the ground. The suitors roared with laughter as they crowded back into the hall.

The Great Bow

Queen Penelope was still unaware of her husband's return. Now Athena inspired her to confront the suitors with a challenge. Her beauty restored by the goddess, she descended the staircase and entered the great hall. Everyone – Odysseus above all – was stunned by her loveliness, and each longed to hold her in his embrace.

"Long have you occupied this house", she said, "in the absence of its lord. Your excuse has been your wish to marry me. Now prove your worthiness. I give you the great bow of Odysseus. Whoever shall be able to string the bow with ease, and shoot an arrow through the rings of twelve axes set in a row, him will I accept as husband."

The great bow was given to the first suitor. He stood and struggled to bend it, but his hands, unused to the strain, grew weary. He passed it on. The next man rubbed the bow with tallow to make it more limber, but he met with no greater success.

Odysseus knew that his moment had arrived. Two of his men, he knew, could be trusted – the swine-herd, and a cowman. To their excited rejoicings, he now made himself known. Then he enlisted their aid, saying: "I intend to get my hands on the bow and its quiver, but these scoundrels will try to keep them from me. Swine-herd, when that occurs you are to carry them down the hall and into my hands. And cowman, to you I give the task of securing the courtyard gate."

Meanwhile, another of the suitors, after warming the bow in the fire, was wrestling with it to no avail. "Let it be!" cried Antinous. "Come, let us have some wine. Tomorrow one of us will do the trick."

"Hear me, suitors to our honoured queen!" said Odysseus. "One small favour I ask. Let me once try the strength of my aging limbs at this task."

His words much infuriated the men, for they actually feared that Odysseus might succeed. Antinous was especially angry. "Is it not enough, you shabby wretch, that we allow you to dine in our midst? Will you listen to our affairs as well? Know your place!"

Penelope rebuked him: "If this stranger has the power to string the great bow, do you think he will demand to make me his wife? Let him try. If he succeeds, I will present him with fine new clothing and armour."

Telemachus, seeing that bloodshed was imminent, spoke out: "Mother, you know that the bow is a man's matter. Go now to your rooms, and I will make the decision, for I am master in this house." Penelope was surprised to see her son display so much authority. But she obeyed, and went to her bedroom, where, as so often before, she cried herself to sleep, pining for her lost Odysseus.

Encouraged by Telemachus, the swine-herd now carried the bow and quiver to his master, as the suitors shouted their complaints. Odysseus received them. He handled the great bow expertly, inspecting it for flaws acquired in his long absence. Then, as effortlessly as a minstrel fitting a string to his harp, he strung it.

Odysseus twanged the string. It sang like a swallow. Without rising from his seat, he aimed at the axe-rings and missed not a one.

The Battle in the Hall

"Telemachus," said Odysseus, "I have not disgraced you." He nodded, and his son slung on his sword and gripped his spear. Odysseus leaped up, and took his stand at the threshold. "Now for another mark!" he yelled, and sent an arrow straight at Antinous.

The point passed clean through Antinous's throat. He kicked out convulsively at the table. Bread and meat were spilled on the floor, to be spattered with the blood which spouted from his neck.

"Never did you expect me home from Troy," thundered Odysseus. "But now you shall be rewarded justly!"

The suitors scanned the walls for their spears and shields, but Telemachus had removed them all. They had only the swords at their belts. One man drew his weapon forth and sprang at Odysseus with a shout, but a whistling arrow sent him slumping to the floor.

Another suitor lunged straight at Odysseus, hoping to dislodge him from the doorway, but Telemachus crumpled him with a spear between the shoulders. From Odysseus's bow hummed arrow after arrow, and the dead soon lay heaped about the room. When the supply of shafts began to dwindle, Telemachus fetched an armful of spears from the strong-room. The suitors cowered behind overturned tables, but accurate spearcasts found their marks.

Suddenly, Odysseus was startled to see a number of the suitors donning armour and grasping great spears. They had found their way into the strong-room. At a cue, six of them pitched their spears together. Surely some would have struck home, had not Athena at this moment made the volley go astray. Odysseus and Telemachus, joined now by the two faithful servants, returned the fire, and four suitors sprawled lifeless. The survivors let fly again. They missed, and the return volley cut them down like the rest.

Odysseus and his allies attacked, and the remaining victims ran like cattle until they were hunted down, one by one, and speared. Finally, all of the suitors were dead. Like fish hauled on the sand by the fishermen's nets, they lay piled in the blood and dust.

Penelope

The slaughter at an end, Odysseus called for the serving-maids, who had been huddling terrified in their quarters. It was their task to remove the bodies, sponge the hall clean, and fumigate it with fire and sulphur. Then Odysseus ordered that Penelope be told of his return.

Athena restored Odysseus to his former magnificent appearance, but added to it even greater height and strength than before. Then Penelope came into his presence.

To Odysseus's surprise, she gave no sign of recognition; she only took a chair silently. "How strange you are," he said. "No other wife could have kept out of her husband's arms after twenty years!"

"And you are strange to me," Penelope replied. "I remember too well the man who sailed from Ithaca. I will command the servants to make your bed outside the bedroom built by Odysseus."

"Who, may I ask, has moved my bed?" demanded Odysseus. "That would be a difficult task, even for the most skilled worker. I know, for I built the bedroom myself, round the trunk of an olive-tree, and the tree itself is the bedpost!"

Penelope began to tremble, as she heard the proof that she had been seeking. Then she threw herself into her husband's arms, and kissed his head.

"Odysseus," she sobbed, "do not be angry with me. I have always feared that some man would win me by deceitful means – so many miseries have the gods inflicted upon me! But only my husband could have known the secret of the olive-tree." She clung to his neck; she could not let go.

Odysseus wept as he held his wife in his embrace. This was the happiness of swimmers, struggling against rushing surf from storm-wrecked ship to stand upon earth once more.

16
AENEAS
WHO FOUNDED
ROME

It was only in 1932 that the Cave of the Sybil was found, its opening having been buried by soil falling from above. Carved with great precision from solid rock, it extends for 150 feet along the flank of the hill of Cumae, which rises abruptly from the beautiful Mediterranean beaches. The secret chamber of the Sybil is at the far end. To look down the corridor at sunset, with the reddish light splashing through at the six openings which face seawards, is to experience a rare thrill.

Near by is Lake Avernus. The surrounding earth must once truly have "groaned underfoot", for these are unstable, volcanic lands. Once there were gloomy forests here, regarded as the home of terrible spirits. But eight years before Virgil began to compose the *Aeneid* (on which this story is based) these ancient woods were cut down to provide timber for the navy of the Emperor Augustus. The lake was linked with the Mediterranean by a canal, and a tunnel – the longest built up to that time – connected the area with Cumae. Perhaps Virgil was paying tribute to Roman engineering when he wrote of the Underworld's mouth by Avernus's shores.

The *Aeneid* is a *literary* epic, and it differs from Homer's epics in several ways. It was meant to be read rather than sung. It displays more complex craftsmanship (Virgil's dying wish was that the *Aeneid,* which he thought still imperfect, should be burned). It gives evidence of greater depth of thought, especially in the Underworld section. And it was written for a political purpose. Until Augustus emerged as emperor and brought peace to Italy, the land had been the scene of bloody civil wars. Virgil reminded the war-weary Romans of their glorious past, and especially of their victories in previous years over Dido's land of Carthage.

In this story you will read about several gods whom you have already met in the Greek stories. Five of them have new names. The Romans had names of their own for a number of the Greek gods and heroes, and the following are included in the story of Aeneas: Juno (Hera), Venus (Aphrodite), Neptune (Poseidon), Jupiter (Zeus), and Mercury (Hermes).

Juno

In a moment, thunderheads erased all brightness from the sky. Crackling lightning ripped the blackness into jagged segments. Storm-winds drove their way into the flanks of the sea, laying bare the sands at the very bottom.

In the middle of the storm, hanging on water-cliffs that pointed to heaven or racing down foaming troughs to the abyss, were ships. And to their creaking timbers clung shouting men – fugitives from fire-blackened Troy – led by Aeneas.

Juno, Queen of Olympus, had brought this storm down upon them. For Aeneas and his courageous band were destined to become the founders of Rome. And Carthage, which some day would be destroyed by their descendants, was the city Juno loved most dearly.

But destiny was not to be thwarted. Even as the waves pounded their way into the hulls of the reeling ships and sent others crashing onto the shore, deliverance came. Neptune, enraged at the turmoil in his realm, leapt into his sea-chariot and sped over the rioting waters. The uprising was soon quelled. With his trident, Neptune pried loose the ships that had been lodged in the rocks. Then, assured that his dominions were in order, he drove his steeds back to their underwater home.

Juno had failed. Furthermore, the tempest that she had created now cast the Trojans ashore near the very city that she wished to protect. A thousand years later, triumphant Romans would burn Carthage to the ground; this visit, by their Trojan forefathers, was to leave the city in deepest mourning.

Dido

Aeneas's mother was the goddess Venus, and a watchful mother she was. On the battlefield of Troy, when Diomedes had Aeneas at his mercy, Venus had whisked her son to safety. When she saw her Trojans buffeted by ill-willed Juno, she had at once appealed to Jupiter. And now, as Aeneas led the Trojans into Carthage, Venus made plans to assist him.

Dido, Queen of Carthage, was a beautiful young widow; Aeneas, when Troy was devastated, had become a widower. For the goddess of love, there was but one thing to do – to arouse in Dido's heart a burning love for Aeneas – a burning, hopeless, disastrous love.

That night, in a torch-lit hall, Dido provided a banquet for the Trojans. After it had begun, a boy came before the queen on her tapestry-hung throne.

"What boy is this?" said Dido, taking him in her arms.

"That is Iulus, my son," replied Aeneas. But he was wrong. Venus had spirited Iulus away, and in his place, disguised so that even Aeneas accepted him as his son, was Cupid. Venus had begun her cunning work.

As Dido embraced the boy, she felt the first pangs of love. She began to talk with Aeneas, asking him question after question about Troy, about Priam and Hector, about Diomedes and Achilles. "Aeneas," she asked, "tell us the whole story of Troy and your wanderings, from the beginning."

"Too painful for speech", replied Aeneas, "is that tale. Yet, if you truly wish to hear of our city's last agony, I shall tell it."

And he began, telling of the horse that wrought Troy's ruin, and of the serpents that had strangled Laocoon and his sons. He told of his escape through the burning ruins of the city with his family – on his back he had carried his aged father, Anchises. At the sound of trampling feet behind him, Aeneas had run faster, but when he looked back, his wife was nowhere to be seen. Frantically he searched the streets, only to have a nerve-shattering glimpse of her ghost.

Aeneas told of the escape of the survivors over the mountains, of the voyage through the Greek islands and across to Sicily. He told of his near-escape from Charybdis, and of his encounter with Polyphemus, whom they had seen at the water's edge, washing his eye-socket. Finally, he told of the death of Anchises, the most admirable of fathers, and of the storm that had brought his ships to Carthage.

The banquet ended and the guests departed. But even after Aeneas had gone, Dido could hear his words and see his godlike face. On the following day she was again with Aeneas, escorting him through the city to show him the crowds of workmen carving, hauling, and raising the stone of great buildings. But now she had no interest in these affairs.

Dido was now on the verge of revealing her love. Often she

would begin to speak, and stop for no apparent reason, leaving words unspoken. And that night she insisted on hearing the whole story of Aeneas's adventures once more. She hung on his every word, and, when he had left, she threw herself upon the couch where he had been seated.

Juno was keenly aware of Dido's plight, but thought that the situation could be turned to her advantage. She spoke to Venus.

"Why do you not arrange a marriage?" she asked. "Dido would become the slave of her husband, and her people would become yours."

Venus knew what Juno intended. Her plan was to turn the Trojans aside from their true destiny – the founding of Rome. But Venus also knew that Jupiter would not allow such a thing. "You may proceed," she said, "though I am not certain that Jupiter will permit such a union."

"I shall attend to that," said Juno. "At any rate, this is my plan. Tomorrow, when Dido and Aeneas go hunting in the woods, I shall send a thunderstorm that will cause them to take refuge in a cave. I will be there to unite them in marriage." And that is exactly what took place.

A winter passed. For Aeneas, it was a winter of abandonment to love, of indifference to destiny. Finally, Jupiter acted.

One day, Aeneas was startled to see Mercury alight before him. "For what purpose", said the messenger-god, "do you dawdle here? If you care nothing for your own destiny, at least have some thought for Iulus, and the Roman inheritance he deserves. I speak for Jupiter." In an instant, Mercury had flown out of sight.

Aeneas shivered with dread. Immediately, he resolved to choose some fit time to tell Dido the truth. Then he commanded his men to make secret preparations for their departure.

Dido was not long in discovering what was happening. She rushed to Aeneas and asked, "Did you intend to desert me by stealth? Were your marriage vows meaningless?"

Aeneas struggled to control his grief. "I never planned to leave you secretly," he said, "but leave I must. My homeland is not here, but in Italy. You came from Tyre to establish your city. Now Rome awaits its founders, who are destined to be men of Troy. Every night, my father Anchises visits me in frightening dreams. The thought that my son might be deprived of his kingdom alarms me no less. And now, Mercury has appeared before me, to make known Jupiter's will. I have no choice."

"Let the gods look upon me!" Dido cried. "This man was thrown upon our shores, and I let him share my realm. What madness! Go then to Italy, for I shall not hinder you!" She turned, and ran from him. Aeneas, though his heart was melting with love for her, returned to his ships.

Dido's one wish now was for death. She knew her fate – when she lay offerings on the altar, the holy water turned black. She poured wine, and it changed to blood. Now she commanded that a funeral pyre be built in the courtyard, and on it placed everything that could remind her of Aeneas. Her excuse was that she was employing magic to give relief to her soul.

Night came, and Dido's agony redoubled, as an ocean of love and grief roared within her. All night she confronted the blackness of death. Then, in the first glow of morning, she looked on the sea and saw the slim black forms of the Trojan ships and the trail of white foam left by their oars.

At first, Dido spoke wildly of making pursuit, of battle and revenge. She prayed for enduring hatred between her people and the descendants of Aeneas. Then she dispatched a servant with orders to prepare for the kindling of the funeral pyre.

Dido placed herself at the summit of the pyre, and there she saw again the sword she had given to Aeneas. She clutched it and threw herself against the blade.

Later, Aeneas, far out at sea on an unswerving course, looked back at Carthage and saw flames mounting to the sky. That they rose from Dido's death-pyre, he could not know.

The Sybil of Cumae

At last the hulls of the Trojan ships slid onto the sands of Italy. Excited sailors flung themselves onto a wide, flat beach from which ascended the steep hill of Cumae. Here, in a huge cave with a hundred gated openings that extended along one flank of the hill, dwelt a great prophetess – the Sybil of Cumae.

While his men scoured the region for the necessities of life – game, spring water, the fire of flint – Aeneas made his way into the Cave of the Sybil. "Priestess," he cried, "long has ill luck plagued Troy and its people. Now that we have reached the soil of Italy, let our miseries end. Give us our promised home."

At first no response came. Within the cave, however, the Sybil was receiving the words of Apollo. She raved wildly, her mouth foamed, her hair flew about, and within her heaving breast her heart pounded. Then the hundred gates, untouched, swung open, and the Sybil's voice reverberated forth:

"Wars, horrible wars, I see. River Tiber froths with blood. A new Achilles awaits you, and Juno pursues you still. Again a foreign bride brings woe to Trojans."

Her fevered lips were stilled, the echoes ebbed. Then Aeneas spoke again: "These perils are not new to us, and more I had expected. One request I have. It is said that in this region can be found the entrance to the Underworld. My father, Anchises, is there. Direct me to him, I beseech you."

Again came the Sybil's booming voice: "Son of Anchises, if you are to cross the waters of Styx and enter black Tartarus, one thing is needed. Within a tree's thick shade hangs the Golden Bough. You must find it and pluck it out. If Fate intends that you should go, the bough will yield easily to your grasp; if not, there is no metal sharp enough to cut that branch."

Aeneas walked sadly away, distressed at the impossibility of his search. But suddenly, two doves descended – the birds of Venus! They flew ahead and Aeneas followed. He had no difficulty in keeping up with them, for after flying a short distance they would stop to feed. Finally, they fluttered up and settled on a tree. Gleaming there in the forest gloom was the Golden Bough.

Aeneas reached up and the bough came away in his hand. Back to the cave he strode with his treasure. This time, the Sybil consented to emerge and accompany Aeneas to the Underworld.

The Underworld

Beside a lake in the forest depths gaped the mouth of the Underworld. So deadly was its sulphurous breath that birds flying overhead would suffocate and drop, lifeless. So the lake's name was Avernus – "the birdless place". Here Aeneas and the Sybil offered up animal sacrifices.

At the instant of dawn, the ground groaned underfoot, the wooded slopes quaked, and baying hounds lurked in the dismal light. "Take courage, Aeneas!" the Sybil shouted. "Unsheath your sword and follow!" The frenzied woman plunged into the opening and Aeneas resolutely hastened after.

Down, down they went, devoured by the earth – down to the bubbling swamp of Styx. Here Charon the boatman poled the dead across the waters. A multitudinous host crowded the near shore waiting for passage, among them many who would never cross – those whose bodies awaited burial. Charon spied the two living among the dead and his white-bearded chin shook as he yelled wrathful words at them. But, at the sight of the Golden Bough, he prodded several of his passengers off the boat to provide space for Aeneas and the Sybil. The rickety vessel creaked as it took Aeneas's weight, and muddy water oozed through the seams.

When they reached the other side, Cerberus lurched forth, barking menacingly. The Sybil threw him a cake; his three heads gulped the bait, and he slumped to the ground, drugged.

Ahead lay a region set aside for a varied group – infants, suicides, famous warriors, those wrongly executed, and victims of cruel love. Among the latter, like a new moon amid dim wreaths of cloud, strayed one whose death-wound bled still. It was Dido.

"Did I bring you death?" asked Aeneas sorrowfully. "I swear, by whatever may be sacred here, that I left you unwillingly. Dido, do not turn from me!" But she withdrew, full of hatred, into the eternal shades.

The way divided. On the left was a grim rampart encircled by a rushing river of fire, whose white-hot fluids rolled boulders along its bed. From within came moans, the clanking of chains, and the sounds of vicious lashings. This was Tartarus, where the wicked endured endless punishment. But the Sybil, after directing Aeneas to deposit the Golden Bough at the crossroads, led him to the left. Ahead shone the Fields of Elysium.

Here, under a sun and stars of their own, on green and yellow sands, dwelt the blessed. Here, in a more spacious, faintly purple air, they enjoyed the pleasures they had known on earth – feasting, racing, wrestling, singing, dancing. And here, Aeneas found Anchises.

Anchises

Anchises turned and saw his son. Tears poured from his eyes, excited words from his lips, and he eagerly stretched forth his hands. Aeneas rushed to embrace him – but in vain. Three times he reached out to clasp his father's neck, and three times the ghost of Anchises slipped through his arms.

Now Aeneas saw yet another river, its banks filled with innumerable souls of every nation. "Who are these multitudes, father, and what is that stream?" he asked.

"These are souls about to enter earthly bodies once more," replied Anchises. "They drink the waters of Lethe, which remove all memories."

"Can it be", said Aeneas, "that some would consent to inhabit bodies once again?"

"Spirit is in everything, my son," Anchises answered. "That is the force which moves the universe. But it is true that the sparks of heavenly fire within our souls are dulled by the flesh that imprisons them. That is why our souls, when they are freed from the bodies which encase them, must be kindled again, here in Elysium. But, after a thousand years, when we drink the water of forgetfulness, we long for rebirth."

Now Anchises pointed out the most gallant of all the dwellers in Elysium – those destined to be the great ones of Rome. He showed them Fabius Maximus, fated to preserve Rome against invading Carthage, Julius Caesar, conqueror of Gaul, and Augustus, who would found another Golden Age.

But now it was time for Aeneas and the Sybil to return to earth, for the sun of the upper world was sinking. At the Ivory Gates, father and son parted, and soon Aeneas was at the ships again.

War

Over a sea quivering with moonlight, the Trojans sailed up Italy's coast. As the moon's pale glintings vanished in the deepening pink of dawn, they saw ahead the swirling current of a river emptying into the sea. It was the Tiber. Joyfully they entered its shady mouth and set up camp.

Aeneas sent ambassadors to the nearest city, called Lavinium. The aged king received them enthusiastically. He had a lovely daughter, Lavinia, who was ripe for marriage, but he had been sternly warned by an oracle not to marry her to any man of her own country. Destiny, he felt, must therefore have chosen Aeneas as her husband.

But Lavinia already had a lover – huge, powerful Turnus, King of the Rutulians – and Lavinia's mother favoured him. Now Juno inflamed the queen with an insane hatred of the Trojans.

The queen's hatred ignited the passions of all the women of

Lavinium. They streamed from their houses and, led by the mad queen, trooped through the countryside, shrieking hysterically. For good measure, Juno aroused Turnus himself. Soon, hungry for blood, he was marching with his army towards Latium.

Juno had still another plan. The keeper of the royal herds of Lavinium had a pet stag who would roam the woods by day, but return each night to its master's door. Juno slyly contrived to let Iulus wound the animal with an arrow, so that it would flee bleeding and whimpering to its home. Its keeper, and soon all the neighbourhood farmers, were infuriated. They armed themselves with crude weapons and engaged a band of Trojans in a brief but hard-fought skirmish.

Flashing swords, like whitening waves under a rising gale, signalled the onset of war.

Rome

That night, Aeneas's sleep was troubled by thoughts of war. As he lay by the river-bank, there appeared to him in a dream, seemingly rising from the leaves of the poplars among which he slept, the reed-draped face of Father Tiber.

"Row up-stream," he said. "You will come to the small village of Pallanteum. There you will find allies." And, with that, the kindly old river-god dropped back into his watery den.

Aeneas wasted no time in carrying out Father Tiber's advice, and two ships were soon navigating the placid loops of the river. The Trojans rowed effortlessly (for the river-god had stilled the current) until the settlement's hills came in view, and then glided ashore at Pallanteum, the village where some day would rise the marble city of Rome.

As they prepared to disembark, a young man grasping a weapon demanded to know their intentions. This was Pallas, the king's son. When Aeneas had reassured him, the two men earnestly shook hands, and then walked together to the village.

For the first time, Aeneas looked upon the site of Rome. He saw the hill that would become the golden Capitol, now a mere thatch of brambles, and at its base he saw the cow-pasture that some day would be the Roman Forum, heart of an empire. After a warm welcome from the king, and a meal of beef and wine, Aeneas's company was quartered in the rude village dwellings for the night.

Early the next morning, reinforced by a battalion of troops led by Pallas, the Trojans made ready to march. They would head north to Caere, the Etruscan city. Here, it was believed, more allies could be found.

The old king, weeping pitifully, clung to the hand of Pallas, who was his only son. He lifted up his voice to Jupiter: "Hear a father's prayers, I beg you. If it is your will to bring my Pallas back to me, give me life; if not, snatch it from me now, so that no painful message can await me." Then, collapsing, he had to be carried to his house.

The Attack on the Fort

Before Aeneas could return from Caere, Turnus led his Rutulians to the Trojan fort at the Tiber's mouth. Like a wolf circling a sheep-fold, he prowled about the hastily erected ramparts looking in vain for an opening. None of the Trojans ventured forth – Aeneas had ordered them to stay behind the walls.

That night, however, two daring Trojan youths tried to penetrate the lines of encamped troops surrounding the fort. They wished to carry word of the siege to Pallanteum. One got past the troops; but, when the other was discovered, the first returned to help. Both were killed. The next morning, shouting Rutulians paraded past the walls carrying, impaled on spear-points, the heads of the two youths.

That day, the Rutulians attacked. Under shields fitted together to form a roof like a tortoise's back, they attacked the walls. The defenders sent great boulders crashing down on them, and a steady rain of arrows and spears. Even Iulus, before being warned to stay out of a man's battle, joined in the defence.

A bloody fight developed over one of the gates, which had opened in the combat. A Trojan finally rammed it shut with his shoulders, but Turnus had already forced himself inside! With one downward slice of his sword he split the face of a Trojan, forehead to jaw; another blow from his flickering blade sent a head, helmet still in place, rolling from its body. But the determined Trojans, spears out-thrust, closed ranks and drove him through the gate again.

The end of day saw Trojans still in command of the fort. And the beginning of the next brought a great shout from its defenders, for from the sea far up the coast they saw flashes, as light glinted from the shield of Aeneas. Soon the war-galleys of the Etruscans were plainly visible, and soon the fleet was making for the shores at Tiber's mouth.

As soon as the ships had beached, Aeneas jumped down into the surf, leading the assault. Turnus hurled his troops against the invaders, but Trojan javelins cut them down in heaps. Aeneas's spears went everywhere: one smashed through a breast, another through a shoulder, leaving an arm dangling lifelessly by shreds of sinew, and another swished into a foe's open mouth.

The Death of Pallas

On another part of the battlefield, warriors from Lavinium suc-ceeded in halting a force led by Pallas. The young prince turned on his men with stinging words: "These are not gods, but men – men like us, with two hands and one life. Strike them down!" He threw himself into the enemy's midst, carving himself a bloody path, plunging his sword into one man's breast, lopping off an-other's head and yet another's hand. Like a shepherd burning an unwanted thicket by setting fires at several points, so did Pallas by heroic deeds fire the courage of his followers.

Turnus, seeing how his line of battle was buckling, hurried to the spot in his chariot. "Fall back", he shouted to his men, "and I will slay this man myself!"

Pallas was startled, but he ran his eyes fiercely over his huge foe and cried, "Now I shall have fame – either by winning your arms, or by dying nobly!" Then he cast his spear with all the strength he could muster. It slammed into the rim of Turnus's shield, and through it to the body, merely grazing his shoulder.

Turnus paused, took careful aim, and hurled his spear. The point smacked into the centre of Pallas's shield, through its bronze and iron layers, through the breast-plate, and into warm flesh. Pallas pulled it forth, but too late, for his life-blood followed. He swayed, then toppled face forward, his armour clanging over his body.

Turnus stood over him. "Return his body to his father," he said. And, planting his foot contemptuously on Pallas's body, he ripped from it the glittering sword-belt.

Mezentius

The news of Pallas's death threw Aeneas into a rage. Like a black tornado he swept the battlefield, searching for Turnus. But he was not to be found, for Juno had led him away for his own protection. Aeneas had to settle for a foe second only to Turnus in might – Mezentius.

Mezentius had once been King of Caere. However, he had gained a reputation for incredible brutality – a favourite method of torture had been to tie together a living man and a corpse, hand to hand and face to face. Eventually, his Etruscan subjects had risen in arms. But he had escaped with his son and taken refuge with the Rutulians.

Now Mezentius, like a snorting boar at bay, found himself facing his Etruscan hunters. They closed in, but he was a deadly quarry, and many an Etruscan writhed in death-agony, pierced by his javelins. Their own spears had as much effect as sea-spray on a granite cliff.

But Mezentius's cruel career was swiftly coming to an end, for now Aeneas took up the fight. A spear whirred towards Aeneas, but he deflected it and fired one of his own into Mezentius's groin. Whipping out his sword, Aeneas bounded forward to finish the deed.

Just as Aeneas was raising his sword for the death-blow, Mezentius's son hurled himself between the two. With his shield he held off the Trojan while his father stumbled away. Then, with one quick thrust, Aeneas buried his sword in the lad's body.

Aeneas, filled with pity and admiration for the boy, lifted his body and placed it in the hands of the Rutulians. Meanwhile, Mezentius, after tending his wound, had raised himself on his horse and galloped full speed at the slayer of his son. Three times he whirled around Aeneas in a wide circle, flinging spear after spear, but the Trojan's shield deflected them all. Finally, Aeneas made one vicious spear-cast, which split the forehead of Mezentius's horse. The creature reared up, kicking at the air, threw its rider, and crashed to the ground, pinning him there.

When Mezentius came to, he saw Aeneas standing over him. Unflinchingly, he presented his throat to the sword, and his life spread over his armour.

Camilla

Night fell, and a truce was called for the burial of the dead. Soon the flames of funeral pyres dotted the land. That night, watchers on the hills of Pallanteum saw a funeral procession approaching from afar, bearing the body of Pallas. A line of citizens advanced to meet the others, parting the fields with their torches. They met. Then, into their midst ran the old king. Sobbing and groaning, he pressed his son's body against his own.

When the truce was over, the Trojans and their allies decided to attack the city of Lavinium. An Etruscan cavalry troop was to lead the assault. When word reached Lavinium of the forthcoming attack, a mounted force was made ready to repel the invaders. Its leader was a girl named Camilla.

Strange had been Camilla's history. When she was but a small infant, her father had fled from a band of soldiers, carrying her in his arms. He had come to a river swollen by flood-waters. Quickly wrapping his daughter in bark and binding her to a spear, he had drawn back his arm and hurled the precious cargo over the roaring torrent. Then he had plunged in, had fought his way to the other bank, and from the turf had drawn the spear, with the baby still attached.

The wilderness had become Camilla's home, a tiger-skin her cloak. As soon as she could walk, her father had put tiny spears in her soft hand. Before long, she could bring down a crane with one stone from her sling.

And now Camilla, the warrior maiden, drew up her cavalry into a bristling line to face the oncoming Etruscans. The space between diminished, the two sides came within spear-range, and then, with a sudden shout, they charged, colliding in fierce conflict. After a moment, Camilla's warriors retreated; then they jerked their horses' necks about and galloped straight at their pursuers. Three times they pulled back, drawing Etruscans with them like stones caught in a relentless undertow; and three times they returned, like ocean waves thundering against the shore to drench the sand.

The third collision was decisive. The two formations were locked together, with each warrior marking out his opponent. Dying men and beasts thrashed in pools of blood, their groans rising above the clanking of shields and weapons. And where the slaughter was thickest, there rode Camilla.

She was blind to everything but the joy of bloodshed. She was blind to the young Etruscan silently stalking her, circling about her, guessing at her next move, seeking the perfect opening for the spear he wielded. She was blind to the spinning spear that flew and struck, to drain her of her maiden blood.

Dying, Camilla leaned from her horse and fell into the arms of her companions. She wrenched at the spear, but its iron point was embedded in her ribs and the icy touch of death chilled her eyes.

Turnus

The Etruscans, seeing Camilla fall, regrouped and attacked; the leaderless enemy broke and fled, this time not to return. Turnus, who had hoped to ambush the Trojans' main force, now spurred on his troops to prevent the Etruscans from reaching the gates of Lavinium. But dusk was falling, and that evening both armies were encamped before the city walls.

Heavy was the pall of gloom over Lavinium that night. Even the queen, who earlier had so wildly defended Turnus's rights to Lavinia, now begged him to give up his claim. "If you die," she said, "I shall follow you." And, indeed, she was soon to hang herself.

But Turnus would not listen. The sight of weeping Lavinia stirred in him a craze for Aeneas's blood. Fire shot from his eyes as he declared: "Tomorrow at dawn I will settle this war – in single combat with Aeneas!"

Early next morning a duelling-area was measured out. The troops of both sides drove their spears into the ground and leaned their shields against them. And then the two men faced each other.

From afar, Turnus and Aeneas cast their spears, and then ran full speed at each other, to meet with a resounding crash of their shields. Stroke on stroke they landed with their swords, so quickly that no one could tell whose skill was greater.

Suddenly, Turnus reared up on tiptoe and brought his weapon down in what seemed to be the final blow. But the blade, when it hit Aeneas's armour, shattered like brittle ice. Turnus had no choice but to run. As Aeneas recovered his spear from the tree where it had lodged, Turnus looked desperately about for some missile. He saw a stone, so large that twelve ordinary men could barely lift it. This he hoisted, ran so as to throw his weight under it, and thrust it at his foe.

But it was with shaking knees that Turnus launched the boulder, for it did not seem that he himself was lifting, running, or throwing, but someone else. And the great stone in its passage met only empty air, and then the ground, short of its target.

Now shifting visions whirled through Turnus's mind: the city, the Rutulians, and the levelled spear of Aeneas. It came at him like a whirlwind, ripping through his shield, tearing into his thigh, and sending great Turnus thudding to the earth. The Rutulians wailed aloud, and far and wide the wooded hills rang with their cry.

"You have conquered me," Turnus gasped. "Lavinia is yours. Carry your hatred no further!" He stretched forth a beseeching hand.

Aeneas gazed on his helpless enemy, withholding his sword. Then his eyes fell upon Turnus's shoulder. There was the sword-belt, the glittering sword-belt of Pallas. Aeneas was terrible in his wrath. "Pallas!" he roared. "Pallas gives the death-blow!" He thrust the blade full into Turnus's breast. The body of the great warrior slumped earthwards, as his soul flew forth and descended, moaning.

GODS OF THE VIKINGS

In northern Europe, farming replaced hunting as a way of life more slowly than in the Mediterranean countries. Where the farmers were most firmly established, however, they left stone monuments of which the most famous was Stonehenge. This group of massive standing stones could be used to compute solstices and equinoxes, and it therefore provided a calendar for the sowing and reaping of the crops. It could also have been used to determine the time of annual sacrifices. The sun-god Balder, who probably dates from this time, was put to death during the summer solstice, when the sun's power begins to wane.

In Scandinavia the tillers of the soil eventually came to be dominated by invaders called the Battle-axe people. They were warrior-herdsmen with male sky-gods – almost certainly another prong of the great Indo-European penetration that sent the Mycenaeans swarming into Greece at the same time. But in Scandinavia there was not any conflict with the farmers' Earth Goddess, as there had been in Greece. She must have been subordinated at once.

The Scandinavian god Tyr is related in name to the Greek Zeus, and to Dyaus in far-off India. But it was Thor who most resembled the greatest of the Olympians. His hammer was the lightning-bolt, and the rattle of his chariot was the thunder. He took as his wife the goddess Sif, whose golden hair was like the wheat, and even today it is believed that his sheet-lightning ripens the grain to the colour of Sif's hair.

And yet neither Tyr nor Thor was chief of the Scandinavian gods. This was Odin, who had gained supreme wisdom by hanging from a tree for nine days and nights. Thereafter he was called the God of the Hanged.

The best-preserved body from ancient times is that of Tollund man, which was dug from a bog in Denmark in 1950. He lived two thousand years ago. Though he may have been an offering to the Earth Goddess, most scholars believe that his death by hanging indicates that he was sacrificed to Odin. The photograph at the right shows the body of the Tollund man lying in the position in which it was found.

The greatest period in Scandinavian history was that of the Vikings, those seaborne warriors who invaded Iceland, Ireland, England, France, and Sicily, and even settled in Newfoundland. An excavation on the northern tip of Newfoundland yielded, in 1964, a doughnut-shaped soapstone spinning-ball – exactly the same as

Universitetets Oldsaksamling

the type used in Norway about the year A.D. 1000. Perhaps it was over-population that sent these brilliant navigators out of the fiords to strange coasts; perhaps it was thirst for trade, or for loot. But whatever their motive, it is certain that the Viking's success was largely due to the excellence of their ships.

Illustrated at the left is a Viking ship discovered in the nineteenth century in the sands of Gokstad, Norway. Within it, a richly-dressed chieftain had been buried around A.D. 900.

These daring men loved to hear their exploits sung by minstrels. It is in their legends or *sagas* that the Viking tradition of heroism has been preserved. The *Eddas* (from which the following stories were taken) tell also of their gods, though figures like Odin and Thor are in many ways more like heroes than gods.

Royal Danish Ministry
for Foreign Affairs

17
THE
WORLD
OF ODIN

Odin is chief of the gods, but he is also, as the Viking tombstone from the island of Gotland shown on page 179 illustrates, the god of fallen warriors. The upper level shows the dead man toppling from his horse on the battlefield. In the next, Odin's eight-legged horse, Sleipnir, seems to be bearing him off. And the third panel shows the hero's triumphant arrival at Valhalla. His ship, with its crew grasping the hanging ropes, occupies the rest of the stone.

Odin, like Hermes and Orpheus, is then an escort of the dead – and thereby recognizable as still another shaman-figure. The shamans of Siberia, in fact, claim to possess eight-legged horses like Odin's. Again like Hermes, Odin has associations with birds – not only with the ravens that flew out each day over the world to bring back reports on all that was happening, but with the eagle perched on Yggdrasill's branches. (One of Odin's names is Eagle.) Still another indication that he is a shaman-figure is his use of the dwarf Mimir's skull to foresee future events – shamans often consult the skulls of their ancestors in the same way.

Another characteristic of the shaman is his ability to gain wisdom by entering a deep trance, and Odin's nine-day ordeal on Yggdrasill, undertaken to gain knowledge of the runes, is an example of this. And the tree on which he hung is his. Its name is "Ygg's [Odin's] horse" – and the gallows, in folklore, have been called the "hanged man's horse".

The warriors dedicated to Odin, called *berserkir*, also entered into a trance. When they fought they frothed at the mouth, howled, and even bit their shields. The fact that they were clad in bear-skins is another indication of Odin's remote origin – as leader in the ancient rituals of the hunters.

Creation

In the beginning there was neither earth nor heaven. Nothing existed: not a ripple of water, not a blade of grass, not a grain of sand. There was only a vast, yawning deep.

Antikvarisk-Topografiska Arkivet (ATA)

But at length a change came about – the north became north, and the south became south. The north was Niflheim, and here a fountain spouted forth and grew into a roaring torrent. From this tumultuous outpour, twelve rivers began to flow, but because the air was cold the waters froze, layer upon layer. The great deep was filled with a crushing weight of ice.

The south was Muspelheim, a land of sparks, flame, and scorching gases. Where the hot winds of Muspelheim blew upon the ice, a dense fog billowed forth, and from the fog fell droplets of water, which contained the first life. This was the giant, Ymir.

Ymir did not long want for food. A cow solidified out of the mist and provided him with milk, and for its own nourishment it licked the salt engrained in the ice. One day, strands of yellow hair appeared in the ice that the cow was licking. By the next day it had uncovered a brow, and, underneath, eyes of the deepest blue. When the cow's hot tongue had rubbed away all of the encasing ice, the eyes moved; soon the head was free, then the torso, and then the limbs. The legs flexed, and the body lurched and rose up.

This being, powerful and beautiful, was the first god. In time a second generation of gods was created, and a third. And in this third generation was one who became the chief of all the gods – Odin.

Odin and his brothers fell into a dispute one day with Ymir, and they struck him on the head and killed him. Then they took his body, and from it they formed the world as we know it. From Ymir's skull, the heavens were created; his brains, flung into the sky, became clouds; and from his hair the trees were made. His flesh became the earth, and from his eyebrows was formed Midgard, one day to be the home of men. Out of the centre of Midgard rose Asgard, the fortress of the gods, which could be approached only by the rainbow bridge Bifrost.

Gallons of blood flowed from Ymir, and these became the ocean, which encircled Midgard. Surrounding the ocean was the land of the giants, which was called Jotunheim. Ymir's bones were its mountains, and his toes were its rocks.

From what remained of Ymir's body there grew an enormous ash tree, Yggdrasill, which supported the entire universe. One of its roots was in Asgard, another lodged in Midgard, and still another extended down to Niflheim, where it was gnawed perpetually by a dragon. From this dragon to an eagle who perched in Yggdrasill's uppermost branches a squirrel ran forever up and down, chattering evil words meant to stir up strife between the two. At Yggdrasill's base also are the well of Mimir, the dwarfish god of wisdom, and that other well by which dwelt the three Fates, who know man's past, present, and future.

Valhalla

Of the palaces raised on Asgard, the largest was Valhalla. Through each of its 540 doors, eight hundred heroes could stride shoulder to shoulder. Spears were its rafters, and its shingles, shields of gold.

Odin decreed that those among mankind who died as heroes should be brought to Valhalla. After a battle the Valkyries, warrior-maidens clad in armour and bearing spears that shot sparks rode across the fields on winged steeds, choosing the heroic from among the slain. In Valhalla each hero drank from the skull of his greatest enemy, and feasted daily on the meat of a boar that was roasted every morning and would be whole again by night. For amusement they fought one another with utter recklessness. They could slash each other to pieces, for like the boar they would recover completely from their wounds.

In Valhalla was Odin's throne. There the great god sat, two wolves at his feet and two ravens, Thought and Memory, on his shoulders. Every day they flew throughout the world, bringing Odin report of all they had seen. He communed also with the decapitated skull of the wise Mimir.

To gain supremacy over the gods, Odin had suffered heavily. He had risked his life to take from the giants a magic mead which gave to anyone tasting it the power to create poetry. For a draught from the Well of Wisdom, he had paid with one of his eyes. And to gain knowledge of the magical writings known as Runes, he had been gashed with a sword and hanged for nine days and nights on Yggdrasill – a sacrifice to himself.

The Brood of Loki

Another who lived on Asgard was Loki, the clever fire-demon. Like the fire he provided, Loki was unpredictable and at times destructive. He used his cleverness to devise all manner of tricks, and his mischief became more and more malicious and spiteful, until he became the foe of the gods.

Early in his mischievous career, Loki fathered a troublesome brood of monsters – three in all. One was the World Serpent. Odin succeeded in throwing him into the ocean, where he grew to such an enormous length that he was able to encircle the world and grasp his tail in his jaws.

Hel was another of Loki's children. A ghastly creature she was – half of the skin of her face was pink, the other half blue like a corpse's. Odin threw her into Niflheim and made her queen of the realm of death. All who die of old age or disease find their way to her icy palace.

The third, and most difficult to manage, of Loki's offspring was the wolf, Fenris. Because of his voracious appetite, he ate and drank himself to a terrifying size. But he grew not only larger, but stronger, uglier, and more vicious as well. Thus, the gods decided that he would have to be tied up.

In a playful mood, the gods approached Fenris with a chain, and asked him to see if he was strong enough to break it. He was. With one lunge, he had snapped it.

A stronger chain was forged, and again the gods persuaded Fenris to try his strength. Another lunge – another broken chain.

Now the gods called upon a skilful dwarf, with a request for a chain that could not be severed. He produced one, from six ingredients: cats' footsteps, women's beards, the roots of mountains, the voices of fish, the longings of bears, and birds' spittle. The chain was smooth and light, but the dwarf affirmed that it could not be broken.

Again the gods asked Fenris to demonstrate his strength, but this time the wolf was suspicious. "You're trying to trick me," he said. "I can hardly see that chain; it must have magical powers."

"So!" jeered the gods. "The great Fenris is afraid to test his strength on a thread of silk!"

"Of course I'll try to break it," replied Fenris. "But, while I am doing so, one of you must place his hand in my jaws."

The gods looked at each other. None was particularly eager to risk placing his hand in that gaping mouth. Finally, the mighty wrestler, Tyr, son of Odin, stepped forward. "There is nothing to fear," he declared, and he set his wrist between the dripping fangs. Then Fenris allowed the gods to use the new chain.

Again the wolf lunged forward, but this time the chain only tightened around him. Fenris paused – then he gave a stupendous heave. The chain held.

The gods, seeing the look of amazement and rage on the wolf's face, began to laugh – all except Tyr, that is, for Fenris had snapped his jaws.

THE WORLD OF NORSE MYTHOLOGY

18
THOR
AND THE
GIANTS

Jotunheim, on whose peaks perch the dwarfs who support the sky, is very much like the mountainous terrain of Norway. And the giants seem to be personifications of its rugged features. There were three varieties of giants: those of the fire, those of the hills, and those of the frost. The latter lives on in its descendant, Jack Frost. The giants were hearty drinkers, and so too were the Vikings. Drinking was, in fact, the chief way of cementing *frith*, the sense of communion among the members of a clan. Little wonder that Thor, prodigious drinker that he was, enjoyed tremendous popularity with the peasantry. He was their protector and the one called upon to make their fields – and their marriages – fertile.

Despite his capacity for drink, Thor represented the principle of order; even today, the gavel of order in Scandinavian courts is called the "Hammer of Thor". And the Vikings, too, had a sure sense of law, for they had plenty of angry disputes to settle. The Vikings' instinct for order shows up even in their architecture, for it was from the clearly proportioned churches built by their descendants in Normandy that the soaring, intricately-constructed cathedrals of the Gothic style evolved.

Time, too, had a well-defined order for the Vikings, based ultimately on the Babylonian scheme for the days of the week. The first two days belonged to the sun and the moon (the king and the queen), and the others were related to the five visible planets and a particular governmental official:

English	Tuesday	Wednesday	Thursday	Friday	Saturday
Norse	Tyr	Odin	Thor	Frija	
Roman	Mars	Mercury	Jupiter	Venus	Saturn
French	mardi	mercredi	jeudi	vendredi	samedi
Greek	Ares	Hermes	Zeus	Aphrodite	Cronus
Babylonian	Nergal	Nebo	Marduk	Ishtar	Ninib
Officers	general	treasurer	premier	priestess	executioner

Thialfi

Thor, the strongest of Odin's sons, had red hair, a red beard, and jutting red eyebrows. He was the god of the storm. His mighty hammer, which returned to his hand like a boomerang, was the thunderbolt; his massive chariot, drawn across the heavens by two goats, was the thunder.

Thor had many adventures, but the best known of them was his visit to Jotunheim, the land of the giants. Accompanied by Loki, Thor crossed the ocean, and by nightfall he entered the great forests of Jotunheim. There the two looked about for a place of lodging. A peasant invited them to stay at his cabin, but, when Thor saw how little food the peasant had to offer, he killed his two goats for supper.

When he had cooked them, Thor gave nourishing portions to the peasant and his family, with this warning: "Here is the best of meat. But don't break open the bones. When you have picked them clean, throw them into the skins."

The poor family was overjoyed to have such a quantity of meat, and they ate heartily. But Loki, mischievous as always, spoke to Thialfi, the peasant's son: "You'll miss something marvellous if you don't have some of that marrow. It will make a man of you! Go ahead – Thor will never know the difference." Thialfi could not resist. With a quick rap, he split one leg-bone and sucked the marrow. Thor, busily gnawing on a shank, did not notice.

The next morning, Thor touched the skins with his hammer. Instantly, the bones took the form of skeletons, muscles grew upon them, and the skins neatly folded around them. The goats were ready and eager to pull the chariot again.

But Thor observed that one of the goats had a slight limp. Guessing the truth, he gave the peasants a tongue-lashing: "You have broken his bones! Now I'm going to break yours!" He raised his hammer to smash every member of the peasant's family, but Thialfi, confessing, fell at his feet and pleaded for mercy. Thor forgave him, but Thialfi from that time forward had to act as his servant.

Skrymir

Thor left his goats with the peasant's family and set out on foot with Loki and Thialfi. That night they found shelter in a very odd-looking place – a hall completely open at one end and with several long chambers at the other.

During the night, there was a terrifying earthquake, accompanied by a monstrous, rumbling sound. The travellers sought refuge in the widest of the chambers. At dawn, when Thor looked around outside for signs of the disturbance, he could actually see the ground shaking and hear the groans it emitted. It was the hill that was acting so strangely – a smooth, rounded hill that looked almost like the stomach of a giant. And that indeed was what it was!

Just then the giant awoke and saw Thor. "Hello, there!" he shouted resoundingly. "You're Thor, aren't you? Well, I am the giant Skrymir. But what have you done with my glove?" The "hall" that the three had entered was Skrymir's glove, and during the night they had taken refuge in the thumb.

Skrymir proved to be a friendly giant, however, and he offered to guide them to the hall of Utgard, the king of the giants, and even to carry their food. All the provisions were crammed into one bag. When they stopped for the night, Skrymir said, "Help yourself to the food," and then fell fast asleep.

Now Thor was ravenously hungry, and he snatched at the bag at once, but he could not untie the fastenings. He struggled and fumed over the strings – but to no avail. Finally, determining to bring this matter to Skrymir's attention, Thor rapped on the giant's head with his hammer. Skrymir woke up. "A leaf must have landed on me," he said, and immediately went back to sleep.

Soon Skrymir was snoring again. Hungry and tired as he was, Thor was so angry that he took his hammer and brought it down on Skrymir's skull with what he thought was enough force to put a dent in it. "What now?" Skrymir muttered. "An acorn, I suppose." And again he fell asleep.

Towards dawn, Thor was so infuriated that he decided to end the whole matter with one decisive blow. He concentrated all his energy in one stroke so violent that he thought the hammer might disappear into Skrymir's head. The giant thereupon sat up, rubbed his skull, and rumbled, "What was that – a bird?" So Thor finally gave up trying to catch Skrymir's attention.

That day, when Skrymir had brought the three to a city in the middle of a plain, he went his separate way. Then Thor and his companions entered a great hall, which was crowded with giants seated at tables.

Blazeaway

King Utgard strode up to the travellers. "Well, if it isn't Two-goat Thor!" he laughed scornfully. "How would you like to give us a demonstration of your powers?"

Before Thor could make his reply, Loki, who was terribly hungry, stepped up and declared: "I challenge anybody in this hall to an eating contest. I can eat faster than any of you giants."

"That," said Utgard, "I would like to see." He then summoned one of his followers, named Blazeaway, to come forward, and between Blazeaway and Loki a long trough loaded with steaming red meats was placed. Loki, cramming meat into his mouth and working his jaws furiously, gave a good account of himself. The two met exactly in the middle of the trough. But Loki had eaten only the flesh, while Blazeaway had gobbled up meat, bones, and his half of the trough as well. He was therefore declared the winner.

Wit

"Your friend isn't much of an eater," said Utgard to Thor. "What can your other companion do?" But Thialfi had already shown that he was a very swift runner, and he volunteered to race. His opponent was a boy named Wit.

Thialfi ran a good race, but Wit beat him by such a margin that he was able to turn around and meet Thialfi as he crossed the finish line. A second race ended with the same result, and on a third heat Thialfi saw Wit trotting back from the finish line before he had gone half way down the track.

The Drinking Horn

"So much for your companions," sneered Utgard. "Now let us see what you can do, Thor. Here's one of the horns we drink from. You should be able to empty it in one swig, although ordinary persons would require two. Of course, anyone needing three draughts doesn't know how to drink."

Thor grasped the horn and took such deep swallows that he thought its contents would surely have been drained. When he had run out of breath, however, he could see almost no difference in the level of the liquid. He was forced to take another draught.

On his second try, he drank and drank until he was wheezing. He pulled the horn from his lips and peered in, but again his labours seemed to have had almost no effect on the level of the liquid. Furious with himself, Thor wrestled with the drinking horn a third time, forcing great waves of the drink down his gullet. But once again he was unable to empty the horn and he threw it down in disgust.

The Giant Cat

"It is obvious that Thor is no drinker," said Utgard scornfully. "Perhaps I should assign him a task that nobody could possibly fail to accomplish – to lift my cat from the ground."

Thor strode resolutely up to the giant cat, which was just then frisking about at one end of the hall. He placed himself under the cat's belly and pushed upwards with all his might. But the big cat arched her back, and, though Thor stretched himself to the utmost, he could raise only one paw off the ground. Again he felt the mad fury of frustration.

Elli

"It is too bad", scoffed Utgard, "that Thor is such a runt."

"A runt, am I?" Thor snarled. "Only allow me to wrestle with one of you, and I'll show you how wrong you are!"

"I'm sorry," Utgard laughed, "but I am afraid that every man here would consider it an insult to be matched with a dwarf like you. But, if you wish to display your wrestling prowess, I could bring in my old nurse, Elli. Of course, you shouldn't expect her to be a push-over, for she's won her share of bouts."

Elli, a bent creature with watery old eyes and toothless gums, tottered into the hall. More shame for Thor! The more he strained, the more she resisted. And when she began to exert herself, great Thor, the son of Odin, was brought down on one knee.

Utgard's Confession

Utgard announced that it was too late to see any more of this display. After treating his guests to a hearty feast, he escorted them to the city gates. Here he revealed a strange thing.

"You will not enter this city again," Utgard said, "and so I will tell you the truth. Your strength is indeed wondrous and you have threatened us all, I must confess, with destruction. The giant Skrymir that you met in the woods was really I. The three blows you gave me with your hammer would have killed me, had I not evaded them so cleverly. There are three deep valleys in the earth now, to reveal your strength.

"Your friend Loki was in truth a mighty eater, but his opponent, Blazeaway, consumes everything. He was Fire in disguise! When your servant was racing against Wit, he was actually competing with a thought in my head – and what is faster than thought? And you, Thor – what anxiety you caused me. One end of the drinking horn was connected with the ocean, and you lowered the level of its waters! As for the cat, that was in fact the World Serpent that encircles Midgard. We were quaking in our boots when you succeeded in lifting it. And your wrestling partner, Elli, was really Old Age, who brings all men low."

Upon hearing this, Thor was roused to the highest pitch of anger. He raised his hammer to shatter Utgard and his city, but, in an instant, both had vanished.

19
THE
DEATH
OF BALDER

This dragon-head, from the funeral-ship unearthed at Oseberg in Norway, seems to express the agony of spirit occasioned by Balder's death. The Egyptian god, Osiris, was suffocated and later dismembered by his brother, but Balder's brother, the dim-eyed god of winter, stabbed the sun-god and burned his corpse.

What is the meaning of his death? One significant clue is the name formerly applied to the fires set on Midsummer Night in Sweden – "Balder's balefires". It seems likely that the custom in earlier times had been to burn a human sacrifice – probably a king – each year on the twenty-first of June. This is the date of the solstice, when the sun begins its retreat towards the south. The fiery sacrifice was meant to acknowledge the sun's decline, just as midwinter fires were lit to encourage it to revive and move into northerly skies again. The latter custom lives on in our Yule Logs.

The wood which fed the blaze was probably the oak, for this was the favourite tree of the lightning-god – his bolts descended on it more often than on any other tree. In the fall its leaves fell off, but throughout the winter some of the oak-trees were wrapped in mistletoe. The mistletoe-dart that killed Balder could have symbolized the lightning shaft.

Because the mistletoe was always green, it seemed to be the very heart of the tree's life – rip it off, and the tree must die. In this dramatic way the halting of the sun's northward progress could well have been represented in ritual.

Balder must once have been thought to have died and been reborn annually, but the Viking warrior's belief in Fate seems to have overruled his resurrection. And the chief obstacle is represented by Loki, who renounces communion with his fellows and is transformed into a fish, like another old trickster of the hunters – Wemicus.

Balder's Dream

In Scandinavia there grows a grass that is whiter than any other. It is so white that it is named after the sun-god Balder, whose face and hair were of surpassing brightness. It was he who was the wisest, the happiest, and the most handsome of the gods.

Therefore it troubled the gods when, one day, Balder was plunged into gloom. He hardly spoke to them, and when he did it was with so heavy a voice that they too grew depressed. Odin, his father, at length asked Balder to say what had cast him into such despair.

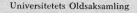

Universitetets Oldsaksamling

"I have had a dream," Balder replied.

"Yes," said Odin, "you often have dreams. Was this one not pleasant like the rest?"

"No, it was not," said Balder. He seemed unwilling to say more.

"Tell me what it was."

"I dreamed", said Balder, "that I would die."

Odin shuddered, but replied at once, "Ah, my son. What harm could come to you? You have no enemies."

Balder said nothing; he only stood with eyes averted.

"You must raise your spirits," Odin said. "I will go and speak to your mother, to see if there is some way of ending your gloom."

Odin went to his wife Frija, and together they tried to think of some way of helping their son. "I know that no one bears any malice towards Balder," said Frija. "But we must reassure him. If only we could convince him that nothing will harm him!"

"Let us have everyone, and everything, swear an oath!" said Odin. "Let them promise never to do injury to our son!"

"Yes," said Frija. "I will tell them."

And Frija went to all gods and men, all giants and dwarfs, all living creatures, all metals and stones, all diseases and poisons, and even water and fire – and all swore never to harm Balder. Only one small plant did she overlook.

The gods were overjoyed to learn that the oaths had been taken. Then they realized what sport it would be if they flung weapons at Balder, for, if all things had sworn not to harm him, surely nothing could pierce his flesh. So knives were thrown at him, and spears and axes. When any of these objects neared Balder's body, they veered off, as if deflected by a stout but invisible casing of armour. Even jagged, heavy rocks, no matter how well aimed, changed course in mid-flight.

The gods shouted with laughter and even Balder forgot his gloom. Only Loki was not amused. He, a mere fire-demon, was jealous of the god of the sun, and it irritated him to see all those missiles causing no wounds. At last he disguised himself as an old woman and went to see Frija.

"Do you realize what the gods are doing to your son?" Loki asked.

"Why, of course," Frija laughed. "They are throwing weapons at him; for nothing can do him harm. I have the oath of all things that he shall be safe."

"All things?" Loki inquired.

"All, except for one small shrub growing on the west side of Valhalla, which is surely too small to be of harm. It is called mistletoe."

Loki left, to reappear later at the scene of merriment. He noticed that Balder's brother Hodur, the blind god of winter, was not participating in the sport.

"Why aren't you shooting?" Loki asked.

"Because I cannot see," said Hodur, "and because I have no weapons."

"Here, take this in your hand," said Loki, handing a small dart to Hodur, "and I will help you to aim it at him."

Hodur took the weapon and, with Loki's aid, threw it at Balder. This time, the missile went straight for its mark, struck, and brought Balder to the ground. He was dead.

It was the mistletoe, of course, which Loki had moulded in a deadly dart and guided into the heart of the sun-god.

The Funeral Ship

Stricken with grief, the gods lifted up Balder's body and carried it to the shore of the sea. There, on Balder's great dragon-ship, a funeral-pyre was built and his body placed upon it. The sight was too much for the god's wife; she cried out in dismay, and sank to the ground, lifeless. When the pyre was set ablaze, her body was beside his.

The dragon-ship was set adrift. Now the wind of evening filled its sails, and sent flames crackling through the wood of pyre and ship. Sheets of flame flared up as the vessel drifted out to sea. The bronze shields lining its flanks splashed into the water, their supports consumed by the blaze, along with the burning dragon-head.

With the onset of darkness the flames reached their climax, their brilliance mirrored a hundredfold by the surrounding waters. Then the glare became a glow, and the glow a flicker, as the spent ship sank into the ocean.

Hermod's Ride

Balder was gone, but Frija still held out hope that he could be brought back. "Who will ride to Niflheim," she cried, "to implore Hel to restore Balder to us?"

Hermod the Swift, son of Odin, volunteered, and his father provided for him Sleipnir, his eight-footed horse that could outrun the wind. Hermod mounted and rode away to a region of towering cliffs and rocky ravines where a black cave gashed the earth – the entrance to the road to Niflheim. Hermod galloped through the entrances, past the blood-smeared hound, Garm, and down into the dank tunnel. Nine days and nine nights he rode, ever deeper and deeper, until, beneath the lowest of Yggdrasill's roots, he came to Hel-gate.

Here Hermod dismounted for a moment to tighten Sleipnir's girth. Then he leapt onto the stallion, dug his spurs into his sides, and fairly soared over Hel-gate into the vast hall of the Underworld. He saw Hel, queen of the dead, whose face was half flesh-pink, half death-blue. And there, too, seated on a lofty throne, he saw Balder.

Hermod went before the queen and pleaded for Balder's return. "I must see", Hel replied, "how great is this love for the sun-god that you speak of. Deliver this message: if all things in the world mourn for Balder, he shall return. If even one should fail to weep for him, however, here he shall remain."

Hermod remounted Sleipnir and climbed for another nine gruelling days until he had crossed the rainbow bridge and entered Asgard again. The gods heard his message and were filled with hope. To every part of the universe they dispatched messengers with one request, and earth, stones, trees, animals, men – all mourned the passing of Balder.

But, when the messengers returned home, their mission all but complete, they found an old witch crouched in a cavern by the roadside. They called out to her to weep for the dead sun-god. "Dry tears will you get from me," she croaked. "I loved him not, living or dead. Let Hel keep her dead!"

The messengers used all their persuasive powers to change her mind, but to no avail. And when the gods had learned the sorrowful news, they knew that this creature must be Loki, for no one else could be capable of such evil.

Loki's Punishment

Their hopes dashed, the gods flew into a violent rage against Loki, but the fire-demon fled in an instant to a distant mountain. There he hid, in a hut with doors on each of its four sides, through any of which he could escape from approaching danger.

One day Loki saw the gods, led by Odin, approaching his hiding-place, and he disappeared immediately through the door on the opposite side. When the gods had searched Loki's cabin, they discovered a fishing-net there, and, suspecting a ruse, they decided to drag the nearest stream. No sooner had they begun, when a huge salmon was swept into the net. It wriggled and twisted and turned, struggling violently to escape, trying even to climb a waterfall. Before it could free itself, however, Thor grasped it firmly by the tail, squeezing it so tightly that the tail was crushed together. Loki had been caught!

His trick having failed, the fire-demon took on his true shape again and was dragged off to a place where three huge rocks stood upright. There he was bound in chains and fastened securely to the rocks. Directly over his head a serpent was suspended, so that the poison from its fangs would drip onto his face.

Only one person took pity on Loki – his faithful wife. She held out a goblet over his head to catch the venom, but, whenever she carried away the brimming cup to empty it, the burning poison would fall into Loki's face. Then, as he writhed in anguish, earthquakes disturbed the world.

The Twilight of the Gods

A time is coming when all the world will be destroyed and even the gods will be judged. The death of Balder is the beginning of this age, which is called Ragnarock, or the Twilight of the Gods. Six harsh winters, unrelieved by a single summer, ensue, freezing the earth with their frosts and burying it with their blizzards. Disorder comes upon the earth, and brother turns against brother, father against son. The mountains quake, the forests are uprooted, and all bonds are severed.

Then Loki and his evil brood are released. The wolf Fenris, fire streaming from his eyes and nostrils, his upper jaw touching the heavens and the lower scraping the earth, leaps forth from the chain which has finally been split. Floods sweep over the land as the World Serpent, spouting poisonous vapours, churns his way out of the ocean. They, together with the Sons of Hel, led on by Loki, advance to the battlefield to meet the gods in a final conflict.

Heimdall, the watchman of the gods, blows a shrill blast on his horn to summon forth all gods and heroes for the combat. As the world ash, Yggdrasill, begins to shake, Loki himself strides forward to meet the valiant Heimdall, and in the desperate struggle they kill one another.

Now Thor grapples with the World Serpent. By sheer courage and might he overwhelms the monster, but falls back suffocated by the cloud of poison spewed forth by the dying serpent.

Even the great Odin falls victim to the evil forces of Loki. He fights with Fenris, and, when the giant wolf has gathered him into his cavernous jaws, Vidar, Odin's young son, takes vengeance. Holding down the wolf's lower jaw with his feet, Vidar grips the upper jaw in his powerful hands and twists it upwards. With a resounding crack the jaw breaks, and thus does Fenris, too, die.

But then from the south the hosts of Muspelheim come, bringing fire upon the devastated earth. The sun turns black, and the stars plunge from the skies. As the earth sinks beneath the ocean's surface, a thunderously hissing steam ascends, and the flame, having fed upon all remaining life, mounts into heaven itself.

But a new heaven arises green from the waves. The cataract falls again, and the eagle flies, and the fish swim beneath the cliffs. Fields unsown bear abundant growth, and Balder returns.

STUDY
MATERIAL

NOTES AND QUESTIONS FOR EACH CHAPTER

HOW TO USE THIS STUDY MATERIAL

The best way of encountering the myths and legends is through oral presentations by skilled story-tellers. Students capable of telling the stories dramatically should therefore volunteer – well ahead of time – to prepare them. These, and also the accounts of archaeological backgrounds, can be given as the year's oral compositions. Sources of material are given in the FURTHER READING sections.

Students could also volunteer to find the suggested illustrations and recordings that are listed under ART AND MUSIC.

The COMPREHENSION AND COMPARISON section provides some straightforward fact-recall assignments, followed by comparison and analysis questions (usually of increasing difficulty) and sometimes by suggestions for creative writing projects.

Wemicus the Trickster

FURTHER READING

1. This Timagami Ojibwa tale is based on one recorded in F. G. Speck's *Myths and Folklore of the Timiskaming Algonquin and Timagami Ojibwa*. This book is now out of print, but there are other excellent collections, such as R. Manning-Sanders's *Red Indian Folk and Fairy Tales* (Oxford, 1960) and H. M. Hooke's *Thunder in the Mountains* (Oxford, 1947).

2. The trickster-hero, whether his name was Nenebec, Nanabozho, Glooscap, Whiskey-Jack, Rabbit, or Coyote, had much the same adventures all across North America. The "burnt moccasins" story was especially widespread. Find out who the ancient trickster-hero of your area was, and tell the class about him. *Tales of Nanabozho* by D. M. Reid (Oxford, 1963) is an interesting account, and Longfellow's *Hiawatha* is based on Nanabozho's adventures.

3. There are dozens of Indian "origin" tales, such as those about the North Star or the porcupine's quills. Several are told in E. E. Clark's *Indian Legends of Canada* (McClelland and Stewart, 1960).

ART AND MUSIC

1. Nanabozho is said to have executed the rock paintings on Lake Superior near Montreal River. These are illustrated in Selwyn Dewdney's *Indian Rock Paintings of the Great Lakes* (University

of Toronto Press, 1962). Possibly a student could find additional illustrations in the family's collection of colour slides.

2. Dr. Marius Barbeau sings Canadian-Indian folksongs on *Folkways* record 3502.

COMPREHENSION AND COMPARISON

1. "Biter-bit" stories are those in which the trickster is tricked. Show how three incidents indicate that "Wemicus the Trickster" is a story of this type.
2. Give three other examples of the son-in-law's skill in avoiding the fate Wemicus has planned for him.
3. This is a folk-tale, not a short story. Explain the difference between these two forms.
4. Compare the Wemicus story with examples of trickster-type slapstick humour in modern entertainment.
5. Write your own trickster or "origin" tale.

The Buffalo's Bride

FURTHER READING

1. This story was first recorded by G. B. Grinnell in *Blackfoot Lodge Tales* (University of Nebraska Press, 1962). It appeared again in a superb account of the hunters' mythology – Joseph Campbell's *Primitive Mythology* (Viking, 1959).
2. Herbert Kuhn's account of twelve European caves in *On the Track of Prehistoric Man* (Hutchinson, 1955) is exciting reading. The best study of the shaman is Mircea Eliade's *Shamanism* (Bollingen, 1964). The reconstructions of ancient hunting rituals in *The Epic of Man*, published by *Life* magazine, are illuminating.

ART

Large coloured reproductions of scenes from the Lascaux caves are available. Study these – or possibly an authentic Eskimo sculpture – for their precise realism.

COMPREHENSION AND COMPARISON

1. When you have gone bowling, you may have found yourself twisting your body after you have sent the ball down the lane, trying to influence its direction. Give two examples of this "sympathetic magic" from this story.
2. Give other examples from your own experience.
3. "Wemicus the Trickster" is a simple folk-tale; "The Buffalo's Bride" is a myth. Explain the distinction.
4. William Golding's novel *Lord of the Flies* is a skilful re-creation of the hunter's way of life. Do you agree with his view that children plunged into primitive circumstances would eventually practise savage rituals?

5. The boar's head mounted on a pole in Golding's novel may remind you of the "totem" symbol of a well-known boys' organization. What are its rituals?

Horus the Avenger

FURTHER READING

1. The only connected account of this myth is Plutarch's *On Isis and Osiris*. Additional details, however, are still coming to light in newly-translated inscriptions. An excellent compilation of these is R. T. Rundle-Clark's *Myth and Symbol in Ancient Egypt* (Thames and Hudson, 1959).
2. Tell the story of Tutankhamen's tomb. C. W. Ceram's *The March of Archaeology* (Knopf, 1958) has a clear account and large photographs. The archaeologist Howard Carter gives his own description of the discovery in *The Open Road* (Macmillan, 1955), edited by R. L. Hale.
3. Eva Meyerowitz's *The Divine Kingship in Ghana and Ancient Egypt* (Faber and Faber, 1960) shows how traces of the ancient Egyptian rituals survive in modern Africa. John Buchan's *Prester John* and Joseph Conrad's *Heart of Darkness* are fictional accounts of African kings – the latter describes a man who is caught up in the rituals of sacrifice.

ART

Much of the art of ancient Egypt illustrates themes from the Osiris myth. One of the noblest portraits of all time, the sculptured figure of King Chephren, shows the wings of the Horus-falcon framing the head.

COMPREHENSION AND COMPARISON

1. Show that this story is a *myth*, by relating the rituals described in the notes to various incidents in the story.
2. Give three examples of Seth's treachery.
3. What were the two searches that Isis undertook?
4. "Truly, truly, I say to you, unless a grain of wheat falls into the earth and dies, it remains alone; but if it dies, it bears much fruit." Explain how this profound saying (John 12:24) applies to the Osiris story.
5. Man's tendency to identify with a slain leader was clearly revealed in November 1963. Discuss this and other examples of man's identification with slain leaders or martyrs.
6. What scene in the Osiris story is similar to one in "The Buffalo's Bride"?
7. The story of Horus's infancy may remind you of a similar one in the Bible. Explain this and other parallels.
8. In the Great Pyramid at Gizeh, the passage leading to the king's chamber points in the direction of Polaris. Why should this be so?

Marduk and Tiamat

FURTHER READING

1. The Babylonian poem on which this account is based, *Enuma Elish,* is well translated by Alexander Heidel in *The Babylonian Genesis* (Phoenix, 1942). This book also provides a scholarly comparison of the Babylonian and Hebrew creation stories. (Read Psalm 74:12-17 for an interesting reflection of the Marduk creation story.)
2. *Before Philosophy* by Henri Frankfort and others (Penguin, 1946) shows why Marduk's special foe was the water, rather than the hot winds that Horus contended with – the flood waters are less predictable in Babylon than in Egypt.
3. To gain some idea of the violence of the Babylonian floods, read Sir Leonard Woolley's account in *Ur of the Chaldees* (Penguin, 1929) of the great flood which deposited eight feet of sediment. His description of the Death Pit at Ur is also interesting.

COMPREHENSION AND COMPARISON

1. Why should this story be classified as a myth?
2. Describe four major stages in the war against Tiamat.
3. According to this story, for what purpose was man created? What is your own opinion?
4. Which incidents in this story may be regarded as primitive scientific "explanations" of nature? (See *Before Philosophy.*)
5. Compare this account of creation with that given in Genesis.
6. Compare Marduk and Horus as kings who overcome chaos.

Gilgamesh Who Sought Life

FURTHER READING

1. Alexander Heidel's edition of the ancient text, *The Gilgamesh Epic and Old Testament Parallels* (Phoenix, 1946), gives a scholarly comparison of the two accounts. N. K. Sandar's translation, *The Epic of Gilgamesh* (Penguin, 1960), also has excellent notes.
2. Robert Herrick's poem "Gather Ye Rosebuds" is a famous expression of the philosophy of *hedonism.* Which character in the Gilgamesh story gives the same advice – to enjoy the simple pleasures of earthly life?
3. The Gilgamesh epic is perhaps the first rendering of the *grail quest* theme, a fundamental one in literature. How does this theme appear in the King Arthur legend?
4. Stephen Vincent Benét's short story "By the Waters of Babylon" tells of a youth who enters New York City many years after it has been devastated and of the people in the vicinity who have reverted to primitive ways. Compare his adventures with those of Gilgamesh.

COMPREHENSION AND COMPARISON

1. Which parts of this story seem to be based on ritual and are therefore myths? Which are probably legendary?
2. Which incidents show Gilgamesh's heroic qualities?
3. Tell how Gilgamesh on four occasions overcame obstacles before obtaining the plant of life.
4. What impelled him to seek eternal life?
5. Gilgamesh has been called the first of the tragic heroes, since it is through pride that he falls. Discuss this view.
6. Compare Gilgamesh with other characters, fictional or real, who are seekers of life.
7. Who are some other characters in fiction who, like Gilgamesh, have a "man Friday"?
8. Compare the flood story in Genesis (chapters 6-9) with Utnapishtim's account.
9. Explain other Biblical parallels: snake and sacred plant, beautiful garden, hairy hunter, strong man ruined by a woman.
10. The complete epic contains far more repetition than this retelling, especially in the Mountain of the Sun and Waters of Death sections. When chanted by the ancient bards, the repetitious passages must have had a powerful impact on the listener. Give examples of the power of repetition from your own experience.

The Will of Zeus

FURTHER READING

1. Most of this account is based on Hesiod's *Theogony*, but the Prometheus material is from Plato's *Protagoras* and from Aeschylus's great drama, *Prometheus Bound*.
2. The many versions of this, and all the other Greek stories, are skilfully assembled in Robert Graves's *The Greek Myths* (Penguin, 1955) and Carl Kerenyi's *The Gods of the Greeks* (Penguin, 1958). There are dozens of popular retellings of the Greek myths. One lively paperback is W. H. D. Rouse's *God's, Heroes and Men of Ancient Greece* (Signet, 1957).
3. Greek mythology contains an Eve-like character called Pandora, and a Noah-figure named Deucalion. Read about them in another book of myths, and tell their stories to the class.
4. At the beginning of his poem *Hyperion*, John Keats describes the downcast Saturn (the Roman equivalent of Cronus).
5. The concluding pages of *Prometheus Bound* are well worth reading aloud. The sequel, *Prometheus Unbound*, is lost, but Shelley wrote a poem of the same title. It too has a powerful climax.
6. In the Bono tribe of Ghana, the king annually defeats the chief blacksmith in a ritual wrestling match. Both the Prometheus story

and George Orwell's novel *Animal Farm* reflect this ancient conflict between craftsman and political strong-man. Does it survive today?

ART AND MUSIC

1. There is a wealth of illustrative material for Greek mythology. Practically every Greek temple, statue, and vase-painting can be related to the myths and legends. The *Life* magazine series "The Miracle of Greece", back issues of which are available, provides large photographs and charts for display.
2. Greek mythology is still an important theme in art. Goya's grisly portrayal of Cronus eating one of his children should not be missed.
3. Beethoven wrote a ballet called *Prometheus,* and used a theme from it in the final movement of his *Eroica* symphony.

COMPREHENSION AND COMPARISON

1. Who are the three successively ruling males, and what fate did each of them fear?
2. What precautions did each of them take, and how effective were they?
3. Explain how Zeus defeated the Titans.
4. Show how Prometheus and Epimetheus lived up to their names.
5. What were the three phases of Prometheus's punishment?
6. Is there anyone else, in fiction or in history, who, like Prometheus, is a rebel, a martyr, and a benefactor?
7. Do you approve of Prometheus's rebellion? Is it ever necessary to revolt against authority?
8. Compare this creation story with the accounts given by the Babylonians, the Hebrews, and modern science.
9. Compare Zeus with Marduk as champions of the gods.

The Olympians

FURTHER READING

1. The stories of Demeter and Hermes are derived largely from the "Homeric Hymns" to these deities; the account of Hephaestus's trick is in Homer's *Odyssey,* and that of Hera's punishment is in his *Iliad.*
2. Read the famous lines in Milton's *Paradise Lost* (Book One, lines 740-6) which compare Satan with Hephaestus.
3. An ancient ballad, "The Demon Lover", tells of a Satan-Hades figure who abducts a girl.
4. John Updike's novel *The Centaur* (Crest, 1963) concerns Olinger High School, whose principal is Mr. Zimmerman, and one of whose teachers is Vera Hummel, the wife of a garage mechanic. Identify these Olympian characters and others in the book (it has an index).

ART AND MUSIC

1. Two of the most romantic areas in Greece are the craggy site of Apollo's oracle at Delphi, and Cape Sunium, where Poseidon's temple stands and where horses were once sacrificed to the sea-god. Display photographs of these places.

2. Botticelli's *Birth of Venus* is one of the masterpieces of Italian painting.

3. Play a recording of Wagner's Venusberg music from *Tannhäuser*.

COMPREHENSION AND COMPARISON

1. Why is the story of Demeter clearly a myth? Why is the Hermes story more likely a simple folk-tale?

2. Most of the Olympians were born in a strange manner. Give three examples of these peculiar births.

3. List the names and functions of the twelve Olympians.

4. Hera and Zeus are remote ancestors of Maggie and Jiggs. Give other examples of the husband-wife conflict in the comic entertainment of today.

5. Compare Demeter with Isis.

6. Compare the methods employed by Apollo's priestesses with those of today's fortune-tellers.

7. Write a story in which your classmates and teachers are transformed into appropriate Olympian characters.

Dionysus Who Gives Ecstasy

FURTHER READING

1. The stories of Orpheus and Midas are based on the colourful accounts in Ovid's *Metamorphoses;* the description of the maenads is from Euripides' play *Bacchae*.

2. Discuss the ballad "John Barleycorn" in the light of the Dionysus myth.

3. What poem of Robert Browning's tells of music that is irresistible to both rats and children?

ART AND MUSIC

1. One of Nicolas Poussin's greatest paintings is his *Orpheus and Eurydice*.

2. Offenbach's *Orpheus in the Underworld* is well known. Of greater importance in the history of music, however, is Monteverdi's *Orfeo* – one of the first operas.

COMPREHENSION AND COMPARISON

1. How do we know that the story of Dionysus is a true myth?

2. In the summer the blazing sun ripens the grapes; in the fall the

year's branches are hacked away. Show how the Dionysus myth represents this.

3. In the initiation rituals of some Australian hunting tribes, boys at puberty are symbolically killed by men with whitened faces, while noise-makers are swung to imitate the roaring of bulls. Then the boys are represented as being reborn from their fathers. Explain the remarkable parallel with the story of Dionysus' deaths and rebirths.

4. What are the initiation rituals of our society?

5. "Ecstasy" means "standing outside oneself". The rites of Dionysus are excellent examples of man's craving to escape into something larger than himself. What are some of the "rituals" through which this escape is achieved today?

6. The Greek historian Herodotus declared that the rituals of Dionysus and of Osiris were the same. Compare the myths of these "dying gods".

Theseus and the Minotaur

FURTHER READING

1. These stories are based largely on the accounts in Ovid's *Metamorphoses* and Plutarch's *Life of Theseus*.

2. Abundant material on the Cretan civilization is available. The reconstructions in *The Dawn of Civilization* (Thames and Hudson, 1961) and in *Life* magazine's *The Epic of Man* are large and colourful.

3. Leonard Cottrell's *The Bull of Minos* (Holt Rinehart, 1958) tells interestingly of the excavations; Mary Renault's novels *The Bull from the Sea* (Pocket Books, 1963) and *The King Must Die* (Pocket Books, 1959) are fictional re-creations.

4. Compare elements of plot, character, and setting in the Theseus story and in Mark Twain's *Tom Sawyer*.

ART

Titian's glowing portrayal of Europa on the bull offers a totally different intepretation from that of Picasso in his Minotaur series of the 1930s. The latter includes a horrifying engraving which includes Ariadne, Europa, Zeus, and the Minotaur; and it culminates in the overwhelming *Guernica*, instigated by a brutal air-raid during the Spanish Civil War.

COMPREHENSION AND COMPARISON

1. Read the notes for this story, and decide whether this is primarily myth, legend, or folk-tale.

2. What were the seven occasions on which Theseus demonstrated great strength and/or alertness?

3. What circumstances led to the death of Aegeus?

4. What are the heroic aspects of Theseus's character?
5. Give five examples of Daedalus's inventiveness.
6. What bull ritual survives in the Mediterranean area today?
7. Theseus, King Arthur, and the German hero Siegfried undergo the same trial in their youths. What is it?
8. In James Joyce's novel *A Portrait of the Artist as a Young Man*, a writer named Stephen Daedalus wishes to escape from the restrictions of the city of Dublin. Why is his name appropriate?

Perseus and Medusa

FURTHER READING

The main sources for this retelling are Ovid's *Metamorphoses* and Apollodorus's *Library*.

COMPREHENSION AND COMPARISON

1. Who are the two "villains" in this story, and what is their fate?
2. How did Perseus obtain his equipment?
3. What elements in this tale are found also in the stories of Horus, Marduk, and Gilgamesh?
4. Try to draw the ugliest of all Medusas.
5. What characteristics do the monsters of the modern horror film inherit from their counterparts in the ancient myths?
6. Compare Perseus with other characters who rescue distressed maidens.
7. Do the conditions of our society make old-fashioned hero-worship obsolete?
8. Which story more closely resembles the typical Western – that of Perseus or that of Theseus?

The Labours of Hercules

Hercules' labours are described in Apollodorus's *Library*; the concluding episodes in Ovid's *Metamorphoses* and Sophocles' *The Women of Trachis*.

COMPREHENSION AND COMPARISON

1. Which of Hercules' adventures revealed his strength? his intelligence? his marksmanship? some other quality?
2. Give four examples of Hera's interference.
3. Why is Hercules the most popular of the Greek heroes?
4. What Old Testament figure ended his earthly life much as Hercules did? (Read II Kings 2:9-11.)
5. Compare Hercules with Gilgamesh, Enkidu, and Samson.
6. Compare Hercules with heroes of American folklore such as Paul Bunyan, Davy Crockett, John Henry, Tarzan, and Superman.

Jason and the Golden Fleece

FURTHER READING

1. The main source for the story of Jason's early life is Pindar's *Fourth Pythian Ode*; for the *Argo*'s voyage, the *Argonautica* by Apollonius of Rhodes; and for the Pelias incident, Ovid's *Metamorphoses*.
2. Read Robert Graves's account of the *Argo*'s voyage in *Hercules, My Shipmate*.
3. The famous "witches' brew" lines in Shakespeare's *Macbeth* should be read aloud.
4. Compare Jason with Bassanio in Shakespeare's *Merchant of Venice* or with Agent 007 in Ian Fleming's *Goldfinger*.

COMPREHENSION AND COMPARISON

1. What train of events impelled Jason to search for the Golden Fleece?
2. On the voyage, how did Jason lose four of his men and part of his ship?
3. Describe four occasions on which Medea assisted Jason.
4. What do Jason and Wemicus's son-in-law have in common?
5. What Biblical story is similar to that of Phrixus's near-sacrifice? (Read Genesis 22:1-13.) *Abraham sack son gous said*
6. Compare Medea with Ariadne.
7. Which of the four hero stories in this section is closest to the Western pattern, with respect to hero, villain, and heroine?
8. Which of the four heroes is the most admirable and why?

The Wrath of Achilles

FURTHER READING

1. The *Iliad* has been translated superbly by Richmond Lattimore (Phoenix, 1951). The ends of Books 6, 12, and 20 are excellent for reading aloud.
2. The story of Schliemann's discoveries is a good topic for an oral composition. Read Robert Payne's biography *The Gold of Troy*, or C. W. Ceram's *Gods, Graves and Scholars*.
3. Read the famous lines about Helen in Marlowe's *Doctor Faustus*.

COMPREHENSION AND COMPARISON

1. Why is this story primarily a legend?
2. What train of events brought the Greeks to Troy?
3. Why did Achilles withdraw from battle?
4. What plan of revenge did Achilles devise, and Zeus agree to?
5. Who were the other gods and goddesses who intervened in the fighting?
6. Make a chart of the varying fortunes of the Greeks and the Trojans: indicate the hero of the moment and the interfering god or goddess.

7. What was the major turning-point of the war?
8. "Pride goeth before a fall." Apply this statement to this and other stories you have read.
9. Who is the greater hero – Achilles or Hector?

The Wanderings of Odysseus

FURTHER READING

1. The death of Achilles is told in Ovid's *Metamorphoses*, and that of Ajax in Sophocles' *Ajax*. The fall of Troy is described in Euripides' *The Trojan Women* and in Virgil's *Aeneid*. But most of this story is based on Homer's *Odyssey*.
2. Coleridge's *Rime of the Ancient Mariner*, Mark Twain's *Huckleberry Finn*, and Falkner's *Moonfleet* tell of other wanderers over water. Compare their adventures with those of Odysseus.
3. Tennyson wrote two famous poems about Odysseus – "The Lotus Eaters" and "Ulysses".

ART

The *Odyssey Landscapes* in the Vatican Museum are among the earliest examples of the "impressionistic" style. The statue of *Laocoon and His Sons* from the same period might be compared with El Greco's treatment of the same theme.

COMPREHENSION AND COMPARISON

1. Which episodes in this story most clearly reveal Odysseus's shrewdness?
2. What were the most frustrating setbacks that Odysseus experienced?
3. Trace a possible route for Odysseus's voyage on the map.
4. The Odysseus-Polyphemus conflict is the ancient one of the underdog's triumph. Discuss other examples of this in books, motion pictures, and real life.
5. Compare Circe with other witch-like figures in this book.
6. Each member of Odysseus's family is a strong character. Describe the qualities of father, mother, and son.
7. In 1934 a Serbian poet recited a poem which he composed as he went along, which was as long as the *Odyssey*. Who are the minstrels of our society?
8. In his novel *Ulysses*, James Joyce narrates the adventures of a twentieth-century Odysseus. The Lestrygon chapter, for instance, describes gluttonous eaters in an inelegant restaurant, and the Aeolus chapter has to do with the "hot air" of a newspaper office. Write your own modernized account of Odysseus's wanderings. ("After the game, I had intended to go directly home. But it was ten long hours before I was to arrive. . . .")

Aeneas Who Founded Rome

FURTHER READING

The entire story, including the imagery, comes from Virgil's *Aeneid*. Two excellent translations of the Roman epic are those of C. Day Lewis and Rolfe Humphreys.

ART

Some of the best Etruscan sculpture is from the City of the Dead at Caere (Cerveteri). The Roman Forum is in ruins, but some idea of its architectural magnificence can be gained from photographs of the set for the film *Fall of the Roman Empire*.

COMPREHENSION AND COMPARISON

1. As happened in the Homeric epics, the gods repeatedly intervene in human affairs in the story of Aeneas. Describe the part played by five of the Latin deities.
2. Describe the main areas of the Underworld, and compare it with that of the Greeks.
3. In what ways does Aeneas resemble both Odysseus and Telemachus?
4. Compare the Trojans' search for a new home with that of the Hebrews.
5. Show how skilfully Virgil introduces the emperor Augustus into a story about a period 1,200 years earlier.
6. Compare the oracle of Cumae with that of Delphi.
7. Compare the Golden Bough with other magical plants described in this book.
8. What other heroes in this book were impelled to action by the death of a friend?

The World of Odin

FURTHER READING

1. Most of the material for the three Viking stories in this book comes from the *Prose Edda* by Snorri Sturleson. Much of it is quoted and analysed in Brian Branston's *Gods of the North* (Thames and Hudson, 1955).
2. Some of the better retellings of the Viking tales are R. L. Green's *The Saga of Asgard* (Penguin, 1960), Padraic Colum's *The Children of Odin* (Macmillan, 1920), and B. L. Picard's *Tales of the Norse Gods and Heroes* (Oxford, 1953).
3. Some modern shamans of Siberia seek inspiration by riding a hobbyhorse, which is a scaled-down version of Odin's steed. D. H. Lawrence's short story "The Rocking Horse Winner" is about a boy who rides a wooden horse to find the winners of horse races.

ART AND MUSIC

1. Viking art is both intricate and rugged. Its interweaving forms are found also in the sculpture of the Romanesque period.
2. Play a recording of Wagner's *Ride of the Valkyries*.

COMPREHENSION AND COMPARISON

1. Tell how Odin and his brothers created the universe.
2. How did Odin gain supremacy?
3. Show how the creation accounts of the Vikings and the Babylonians reflect the geography of the areas they inhabit.
4. What are the qualities considered worthy of reward by the Vikings? by ourselves?
5. Compare Odin with other shaman figures in this book.

Thor and the Giants

FURTHER READING

1. Read of Thor's other adventures in one of the books listed in the previous section. Especially interesting are those in which he obtains his hammer, and later a great ale-cauldron, from the giants.
2. Compare the Viking style of story-telling with that of J. R. R. Tolkien in *The Lord of the Rings*.

COMPREHENSION AND COMPARISON

1. Describe the four humiliations of Thor.
2. How did Utgard explain each of these?
3. Show how Thor resembles both Zeus and Hercules.
4. Show how elements of the North American hunters' world appear in this tale.
5. Write your own Gulliver-in-Brobdignag account of entry into a giants' world.

The Death of Balder

FURTHER READING

1. The new edition of J. G. Frazer's classic *The Golden Bough*, with notes by T. H. Gaster (Doubleday Anchor, 1961), is well worth reading for its account of this and other myths in this book.
2. The third chapter of Hardy's novel *The Return of the Native* contains a powerful description of a seasonal festival in the Stonehenge area.
3. A seventh-century poem called *The Dream of the Rood* blends Balder with Christ.

ART AND MUSIC

1. The Viking ships are so beautiful that they are illustrated in many

art books. There is an excellent section on them in F. R. Donovan's *The Vikings* (Harper and Row, 1964).

2. Perhaps the most magnificent of all myth-inspired music is Wagner's opera *Die Götterdämmerung (The Twilight of the Gods)*. The closing section especially deserves playing. In it, the wife of the hero, Siegfried, throws herself on his funeral pyre, while at the same time Asgard and the gods are being consumed in flames.

COMPREHENSION AND COMPARISON

1. How did Loki bring about the death of Balder?
2. The Viking word "hel" is closely related to our term "hell". Describe the Scandinavian underworld and compare it with that of the Greeks and the Romans.
3. What were the fates of Odin, Thor, and Loki to be?
4. How was Balder's return to come about?
5. Compare Balder's death with that of Hercules.
6. Explain why this story is a myth, while that of Thor is probably a simple folk-tale.
7. Many ancient peoples had annual rituals of renewal. Some have seen in our own "rituals" involving automobiles a similar striving for renewal. Discuss this and other examples of such rituals.
8. Compare Loki with the other trickster-heroes in this book, and compare Balder with the other martyrs.
9. Which character in this book is both trickster-hero and martyr?

AIDS TO FURTHER STUDY

A PAPERBACK LIBRARY OF BASIC MYTHOLOGY BOOKS

Joseph Campbell, *The Hero with a Thousand Faces* (Meridian, 1956)
Ernst Cassirer, *An Essay on Man* (Anchor, 1944)
H. R. Ellis-Davidson, *Gods and Myths of Northern Europe* (Penguin, 1964)
Henri Frankfort *et al.*, *Before Philosophy* (Penguin, 1946)
J. G. Frazer, *The New Golden Bough* (Anchor, 1961)
Michael Grant, *Myths of the Greeks and Romans* (Mentor, 1962)
Robert Graves, *The Greek Myths* (Penguin, 1955)
Homer, *The Iliad*, translated by R. Lattimore (Phoenix, 1951)
Carl Kerenyi, *The Gods of the Greeks* (Penguin, 1951)
S. N. Kramer, ed., *Mythologies of the Ancient World* (Anchor, 1961)
B. Malinowski, *Magic, Science and Religion* (Anchor, 1948)
Lord Raglan, *The Hero* (Vintage, 1936)
Arnold van Gennep, *The Rites of Passage* (Phoenix, 1960)

THE HERO PATTERN

Reference has been made several times in this book to a pattern of adventures that is followed by certain gods and heroes. Below, the stages in the pattern of adventures followed by Horus have been listed:

Insecure Youth	Death-Struggle	Underworld	Sacred Marriage	Kingly Rule
basket	Seth	Abydos	Hathor	Egypt

Now indicate in a similar way the phases each of the following gods or heroes passes through (only Horus goes through all five): Osiris, Marduk, Gilgamesh, Zeus, Persephone, Dionysus, Theseus, Perseus, Hercules, Jason, Odysseus, Aeneas, Odin, and Balder.

MYTHOLOGICAL ALLUSIONS

If you have studied a Shakespearean play, you may have noticed references to the myths. This was true of most of the poetry of Shakespeare's time, including the great Elizabethan epic, Spenser's *Faerie Queene*. Explain the mythological references in the following lines from Spenser's poem:

1. Whose many heads out budding ever new,
   Did breed him endless labour to subdue:

2. Deep was he drenched to the utmost chin,
   Yet gaped still, as coveting to drink
   Of the cold liquor, which he waded in,

3. Her mighty charms, her furious loving fit,
   His goodly conquest of the golden fleece,

4. Or as the Cyprian goddess, newly born
   Of the Ocean's fruitful froth, did first appear:

5. It fortuned, fair Venus having lost
   Her little son, the winged god of love,

6. Anchises' son, begot of Venus fair,

7. Come home to her in piteous wretchedness,
   After long travel of full twenty years,
   That she knew not his favour's likeness,
   For many scars and many hoary hairs,

8. Which brought that land to his subjection,
   Through his three bodies' power, in one combined;

9. Brought forth with him the dreadful dog of hell,

SUPPLY THE MISSING NAME

Copy and complete the following sentences in your notebook:

1. _____ was inflated by the winds.
2. _____ was born in a heart.
3. _____ was transformed by a girl.
4. _____ made an ark.

5. _____ hunted wild boar by moonlight.
6. _____ put her baby in a basket.
7. _____ swallowed his children.
8. _____ had a liver ailment.
9. _____ had a wife who left him every year.
10. _____ gave her father a headache.
11. _____ hated Peeping Toms.
12. Curiosity killed _____ .
13. _____ turned his dog into a statue.
14. _____ was on a wheel of fire.
15. _____ burned up in space.
16. _____ was too tall.
17. Black meant death for _____ .
18. Gold flakes loved _____ .
19. A horse grew from _____ .
20. _____ used a death-ray on Polydectes.
21. The _____ became a coat.
22. _____ was Siamese triplets.
23. Water flowed from the beard of _____ .
24. _____ had unpleasant meals.
25. _____ was boiled to death.
26. _____ judged a beauty contest.
27. Zeus almost married _____ .
28. Agamemnon took _____ away from Achilles.
29. _____ fought the gods.
30. _____ carried the body of Achilles.
31. _____ guessed what the wooden horse contained.
32. The _____ were addicts.
33. Nobody hurt _____ .
34. _____ yelped like a puppy.
35. Odysseus struck _____ on the jaw.
36. _____ was required to marry a foreigner.
37. _____ had flown through the air when she was a baby.
38. _____ had a two-tone face.
39. The glove of _____ was a hall.
40. _____ killed his brother with a plant.

MYTHOLOGY IN MODERN LIFE

Copy the following in your notebook, filling in the missing letters. Refer to the names in the list that follows:

1. _____ sday.
2. _____ heel.
3. _____ an task.
4. _____ ized tires.
5. _____ ic games.

6. _____ izing desserts.
7. _____ tic situation.
8. Nike- _____ anti-missile missile.
9. _____ tial law.
10. John Glenn's _____ capsule.
11. Oatmeal _____ al.
12. Astro _____ s.
13. _____ y around the world.
14. _____ tically sealed.
15. _____ River.
16. _____ an Sea.
17. _____ ian depths.
18. The sinking of the _____ ic.
19. The wealthy _____ crat.
20. _____ ium 235.
21. _____ al dose.
22. _____ analian feasts.
23. _____ ography.
24. By _____ !
25. _____ rocket.
26. _____ ic-stricken.

Aegeus, Achilles, Amazon, Argonaut, Atlas, Bacchus, Ceres, Chaos, Gaia, Hercules, Hermes, Jove, Lethe, Mars, Mercury, Odysseus, Olympus, Pan, Pluto, Styx, Tantalus, Thor, Titan, Uranus, Vulcan.

MYTHOLOGY BASEBALL

The four corners of the room are home plate and the three bases. The first batter stands at home plate, which should be in the right front corner of the room. He is asked a mythology question by the pitcher, who may stand near the centre of the room. If the batter does not answer the question correctly, the catcher is given an opportunity to do so. The batter is declared out if the catcher gives the proper answer. Otherwise, the batter gets a chance to answer another question.

If the batter gives the correct reply, he goes to first base. There he is asked another question. If he gives the right answer, he advances to second base. If he does not, and the first-baseman does, he is out. The same procedure is followed at second base, and at third. A run is scored if he is successful at both places.

When three batters are out, the side is retired and the other team goes to bat. To keep the game moving quickly, make the questions uninvolved. "Name and describe the twelve labours of Hercules", for example, would require a very long answer.

FAMILY TREE OF THE GODS AND HEROES

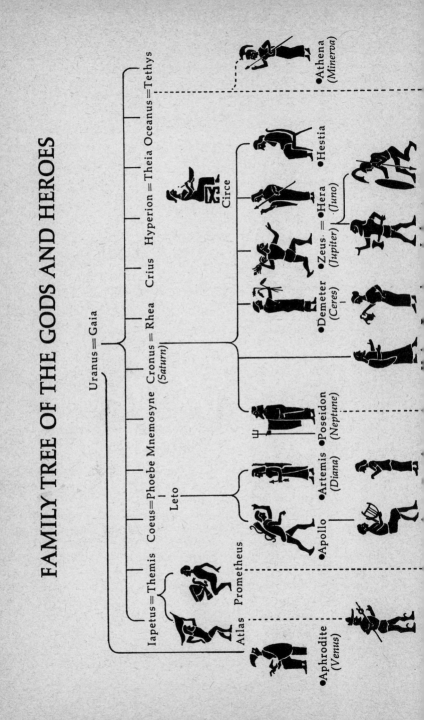

Uranus = Gaia

Iapetus = Themis Coeus = Phoebe Mnemosyne Cronus = Rhea Crius Hyperion = Theia Oceanus = Tethys
(Saturn)

Leto

Atlas Prometheus

Circe

•Aphrodite
(Venus)

•Apollo •Artemis •Poseidon
(Diana) (Neptune)

•Demeter •Zeus. = •Hera •Hestia
(Ceres) (Jupiter) (Juno)

•Athena
(Minerva)

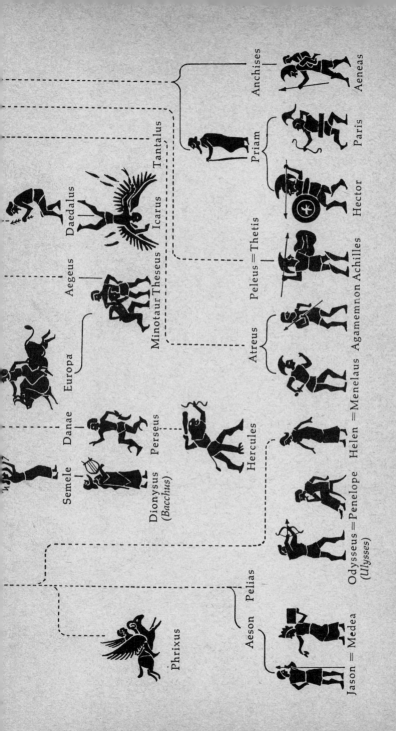

Daedalus   Icarus   Tantalus   Anchises

Aegeus   Minotaur Theseus   Peleus = Thetis   Priam   Aeneas

Europa   Atreus   Hector   Paris

Semele   Danae   Perseus   Hercules

Dionysus
(Bacchus)

Phrixus

Aeson   Pelias

Jason = Medea   Odysseus = Penelope   Helen = Menelaus   Agamemnon   Achilles
         (Ulysses)

HEROES, VILLAINS, AND FOOLS

Listed below are some of the "popular American social types" classified by O. E. Klapp in his book *Heroes, Villains, and Fools* (Prentice-Hall, 1962). See how many you can find from each of the three sources.

	Myth and Legend	Literature	Real Life
HEROES:			
Strong Man	Enkidu		
Top Dog			Napoleon
Underdog			Charles Lindbergh
Smart Operator		Tom Sawyer	
Love Queen			Marilyn Monroe
Athlete			Babe Ruth
Playboy			Errol Flynn
Goodfellow		Falstaff	
Defender			Dag Hammarskjöld
Crusader			Billy Graham
Martyr		Sidney Carton	
Benefactor			Jonas Salk
VILLAINS:			
Rebel			James Dean
Rogue		Don Juan	
Oppressor			Stalin
Selfish Grabber		Scrooge	
Monster		Frankenstein	
Traitor			Judas
Sneak Attacker			Tojo
Corrupter		Iago	
FOOLS:			
Rash Fool		Don Quixote	
Dupe			Chamberlain
Coward		Andrew Aguecheek	
Boaster			Cassius Clay

PRONOUNCING
INDEX

1. The stress mark mark (′) indicates the syllable that bears the principal stress, e.g. *o′ ver*.
2. A horizontal bar over a vowel indicates that the vowel is long and should be pronounced as follows: *ā* as in *ace*, *ē* as in *eve*, *ī* as in *ice*, *ō* as in *so*, *ū* as in *use* (or as *oo* in *too*, where indicated), *y* as in *by*.
3. Diphthongs are pronounced as follows, unless indicated otherwise: *ae* as *ee* in *seed*, *ai* as *i* in *high*, *au* as *au* in *caught*, *ei* as *ei* in *reign* or as *ei* in *receive*, *eu* as *you* (sometimes also as two separate sounds, e.g. *Per′se us, Or′ phe us, The′ se us*), *oe* as *ee* in *seed*.
4. Short *y* is pronounced as the *y* in *myth*, unless indicated otherwise.
5. Pronounce *c* and *ch* as *k*, and *g* as the *g* in *gale* (not as the *g* in *gem*) unless indicated otherwise.

A chel ō′ us, 95, 104

A chil′ lēs, 120-37, 139, 148-9, 161, 164

A cri′ si us, 88-9, 94

Ac tae′ on, 64

A dō′ nis, 139

Ae ē′ tēs, 107, 112-15

Ae′ geus, 80-1, 83-6

Ae nē′ as, 126-7, 159-73

Ae′ son, 108-9

A ga mem′ nōn, 118-20, 123-5, 128, 131, 133, 141-2, 148

Ā′ jax, 120, 122, 129-32, 136, 139, 149

Alc mē′ nē, 96

A′ ma zons, 100-1, 107, 136

An chī′ sēs, 161, 162, 164-6

An dro′ ma chē, 127-8, 135

An dro′ me da, 87, 93

An ti′ nō us, 154-7

A′ nū (oo), 33, 40, 43

A phrō dī′ tē (*see also* Venus), 47, 58, 62-3, 65, 66, 112, 121-3, 126, 129, 160, 184

A pol′ lō, 47, 49, 64-6, 71, 73-4, 87, 95, 121, 124, 127, 132, 134, 136, 163

Ap' sū (oo), 33-4

Ap syr' tus (sur), 115

Ā' rēs (see also Mars), 49, 62-3, 65, 66, 113, 121, 127, 184

Ar' gō nauts, 110-16

A ri ad' nē, 83-5

Ar' te mis (see also Diana), 47, 49, 58, 64, 65, 98, 116

As' gard, 180, 194

As tar' tē, 27-8

A thē' na, 47, 49, 58, 63-4, 65, 91, 112, 121-2, 125-7, 133, 134, 140-2, 151, 153, 157-8

At' las, 50, 53, 102-3

Au gē' as, 99

Bal' der, 175, 190-6

Bif' rost (ee), 180

Blaze' a way, 187, 189

Brī sē' is, 125

Ca lā' is, 110-11

Ca lyp' sō, 151-2

Ca mil' la, 170-2

Cas san' dra, 142

Cer' ber us (ser), 72-3, 103-4, 165

Chā' os, 50

Chā' ron, 71-3, 103, 164-5

Cha ryb' dis, 138, 150, 161

Chī' ron, 123

Chry sē' is, 124-5

Cir' cē (sur see), 139, 146-50

Cly tem nes' tra, 123, 148

Crō' nus (see also Saturn), 50, 51-3, 56, 60, 61, 62, 69, 121, 184

Cū' pid, 112-13, 161

Cy clō' pēs (sie), 51, 53, 138, 143-5

Dae' da lus, 75, 79-80

Da' na ē, 88, 89-90

Da nā' i dēs, 72

Dei a nei' ra, 104-5

De mē' ter, 49, 58-60, 65

Dī a' na (see also Artemis), 58

Dī′ dō, 159, 160-3, 165
Dī o mē′ dēs, 122, 126-7, 129, 131, 160, 161
Dī o nȳ′ sus, 49, 67, 69-74
Dȳ′ aus, 50, 175

Ē′ a, 33-4, 43
El′ li, 188-9
E ly′ si um, 165, 166
En ki′ dū (oo), 37-41, 95
E pi mē′ theus, 54
Ē′ ris, 121
Eu rō′ pa, 78, 79
Eu ry′ di cē (see), 71-3, 110
Eu rys′ theus, 97-104

Fates, 54
Fa ther Tī ber, 167
Fen′ ris, 182-3, 195-6
Fri′ ja, 184, 192-3

Gai′ a, 50-3, 101
Garm, 194
Gē′ ry on, 101
Gil′ ga mesh, 37-45, 77, 120
Gor′ gons, 90-2
Grey hags, 91-2

Hā′ dēs, 59-60, 72, 103, 124, 132, 134, 135, 148
Har′ pies, 111
Ha′ thor, 30, 78
Hec′ tor, 117, 120, 125, 127-36, 142, 161
Hec′ ū ba, 142, 161
Heim′ dall (hay), 196
Hel, 182, 193-5
He′ len, 117, 122-3, 125-7, 142
Hē phaes′ tus, 47, 49, 61-3, 65, 121, 132-3
Hē′ ra (see also Juno), 49, 58-65, 68-9, 79, 95, 97, 101, 102, 112, 121-2, 129-30, 160
Her′ cū lēs, 76, 95-106, 110-11
Her′ mēs (see also Mercury), 49, 56, 65-6, 91, 95, 121-2, 134, 135, 147, 160, 178, 184

Her' mod, 193-4
Hes per' i dēs, 102
Hes' ti a, 55, 59, 64, 65
Hip po' ly ta, 100-1
Hō' dur, 193
Hō' rus, 2, 22-31, 50, 78
Hum ba' ba, 37, 39-40
Hun' dred-han' ded Gī' ants, 51, 53
Hȳ' dra, 98, 105
Hȳ' las, 110-11
Hȳ pē' ri on, 148, 150-1

I' ca rus, 80
Ī' rus, 155
Ish' tar, 40-1, 44, 58, 184
Ī' sis, 23, 27-30
I ū' lus, 161
Ix' i on, 72

Jā' son, 76, 107-16, 121
Jo' tun heim (yotunhaym), 180, 184, 185
Jū' nō, 160-2, 166-7
Jū' pi ter (see also Zeus), 50, 160, 162, 168, 184

Kin' gū (oo), 34-6
Kū mar' bi, 50

Lā o' cō on, 140-1, 161
La vin' i a, 166, 172-3
Les' try gons, 138, 146
Lē' thē, 166
Lē' tō, 64
Lō' ki, 181-2, 185-7, 189, 190, 192-6

Mae' nads, 73-4
Ma' ni tū (oo), 15
Mar' duk, 2, 23, 32, 34-6, 50, 95, 184
Mars (see also Ares), 184
Mē dē' a, 108, 112-16
Me dū' sa (oo), 75, 87, 90-3, 94, 103
Me ne lā' us, 123, 125-6, 129, 142
Mer' cū ry (see also Hermes), 160, 162, 184

Me zen' ti us, 169-70

Mī' das, 69-70

Mid' gard, 180, 189

Mi' mir, 178, 181

Mī' nos, 78-9, 80, 84

Mi' nō taur, 75-6, 78, 79-80, 83-5, 95

Mus' pel heim (hay), 180, 196

Nau si cā' a, 152-3

Ne' bo, 184

Ne' ne bec, 7, 8

Nep' tūne (see also Poseidon), 160

Ner' gal, 184

Nes' sus, 104-5

Nifl' heim (neefulhaym), 180-2, 193

Ni' nib, 184

Ō cē a' nus (see), 101, 171

Ō' din, 175-85, 191-2, 194-6

O dys' seus, 120, 122, 124, 129, 131, 136, 138-58

O lym' pus, 47, 50, 53, 55, 58, 59, 61, 62, 65, 106, 112, 113, 136, 151, 160

Or' pheus, 71-4, 103, 110, 115, 178

Ō sī' ris, 22-31, 139, 190

Pal' las, 167-71, 173

Pan, 54

Pa' ris, 122-3, 125-7, 129, 136, 142

Pa trō' clus, 131-3, 135

Pe' ga sus, 92

Pē' leus, 121

Pē' li as, 108-9, 116

Pē ne' lo pē, 151, 155-8

Per se' pho nē, 58-60, 72, 147

Per' seus, 76, 87-94, 96

Phi' neus, 111

Phrix' us, 107-9, 114

Po ly dec' tēs, 90, 93-4

Po ly phē' mus, 139, 143-5, 161

Pō sei' don (sī) (see also Neptune), 47, 49, 59, 63-6, 93, 121, 142, 148, 151-2, 160

Prī' am, 117-18, 122, 125, 134-6, 140-2, 161

Prō crus' tēs, 83
Prō mē' theus, 50, 54-7, 101-2, 121
Pȳ' thon, 64-5, 87

Rhē' a, 51-2, 69

Sa' turn (*see also* Cronus), 184
Scyl' la (sil), 138, 150
Se' me lē, 68-9
Seth (*see also* Typhon), 2, 21, 23, 24, 26-30, 50, 139
Si dū' ri, 37, 42
Sif, 175
Sī lē' nus, 70
Sī' non, 140-1
Sī' rens, 149
Si' sy phus, 72
Skry' mir, 185-6
Sleip' nir (slay), 178, 194
Sy' bil, 159, 163-6
Sym plē' ga dēs, 111-12

Tam' muz, 40
Tan' ta lus, 72
Tar' ta rus, 57, 59-60, 66, 71, 123, 150, 164-5
Te le' ma chus, 153-7
The' mis, 121
Thē' seus, 75, 78, 81-6, 95, 122
The' tis, 121, 123, 125, 131, 132
Thi al' fi, 185-7
Thor, 175, 177, 184-9, 196
Ti' a mat, 32-6
Ti rē' si as, 96, 147-9, 151, 153
Tī' tans, 50-7, 59, 64, 65, 69, 101-2, 148
Tur' nus, 166-9, 172-3
Tȳ' phon (*see also* Seth), 50, 53-4
Tyr (tur), 175, 182-3, 184

Ū rā' nus, 50-1, 53, 56, 61, 62, 121
Ut' gard, 186-9
Ut na pish' tim, 41-5

Val hal' la, 178, 181

Val ky' ries, 181

Vē' nus (*see also* Aphrodite), 160-2, 164, 184

Vi' dar, 196

We' mi cus, 8-14, 16, 190

Wit, 187, 189

Yah' weh, 48

Ygg (*see also* Odin), 178

Ygg' dra sill, 178, 180-1, 194, 196

Y' mir (ee'), 180

Zē' tēs,   110-11

Zeus (oo), 48-56, 58-61, 63-6, 68-9, 79, 85, 89-90, 96,
    99, 102, 105-6, 109, 121, 125, 127-35, 145, 151, 160,
    175, 184